1195
11/89

D0978051

The Ghost of Peppermint Flats

The Ghost of Peppermint Flats and Other Stories

Ted Stone

Western Producer Prairie Books
Saskatoon, Saskatchewan

Copyright © 1989 by Ted Stone
Illustrations copyright © 1989 by Martha Jones
Western Producer Prairie Books
Saskatoon, Saskatchewan

Cover illustration by Martha Jones
Cover design by Warren Clark/GDL

Printed in Canada
10 9 8 7 6 5 4 3 2 1

The publisher acknowledges the support received for this publication from the Canada Council.

Western Producer Prairie Books is a unique publishing venture located in the middle of western Canada and owned by a group of prairie farmers who are members of the Saskatchewan Wheat Pool. From the first book in 1954, a reprint of the serial originally carried in the weekly newspaper *The Western Producer*, to the book before you now, the tradition of providing enjoyable and informative reading for all Canadians is continued.

Canadian Cataloguing in Publication Data

Stone, Ted, 1947–
    The ghost of Peppermint Flats and other stories

    ISBN: 0–88833–299–8

I. Title
PS8587.T653G5 1989   C813/.54   C89–098131–0
PR9199.3.S865G5 1989

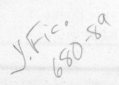

For Laura, Karen, and Heather

Introductory Note

Most of the stories in this book have grown, in one way or another, from stories I've told out loud to audiences in schools and libraries. Many are rooted in traditional folklore. Even the stories that have never been told out loud, however, owe a debt to traditional oral tales.

Contents

Twelve Times Around a Grave

"If you want to see a real ghost," Melvin told Bobby, "what you have to do is go to a cemetery at night. Go to the last grave and walk around it backwards twelve times."

It was me and Melvin Michaels who did it. We were the ones who came up with the idea for getting Bobby Sherman to sleep all night in the old Conolly house. Everybody said it was haunted and Bobby said he wasn't afraid.

Of course, Bobby Sherman used to say he wasn't afraid of anything. That's why we dared him to do it. He'd already climbed to the top of the water tower, and before that he waded through the middle of Carsons' swamp and got bloodsuckers all over his legs. One bloodsucker even crawled inside his underpants.

Another time, Bobby hid in the opening underneath the railroad bridge while the train went over. Nobody else would do that. For a while, it just seemed like Bobby would do anything. He was a real fool when it came to taking a dare.

I guess it started after school let out for the summer. Bobby would dare Melvin to do stuff. Then, when Melvin wouldn't do it, Bobby would do it himself just to show Melvin up. I told Melvin not to let Bobby's teasing bother him, but of course, with Melvin, absolutely everything bothers him.

It was Bobby who first got the idea about ghosts. He said the old Conolly house was haunted and we should go in and look for money and treasures. He said he had a skeleton key that would open any lock. He said he could get in that house whenever he wanted. Then he dared Melvin to go in first.

Normally, I don't pay any attention when Bobby dares Melvin to do something. But getting into a haunted house sounded kind of interesting. Besides, I'd never heard of skeleton keys and I wanted to know how they worked.

"There's nothing to them," Bobby said. "Skeleton keys are just old keys that used to belong to detectives and robbers before they got killed. They'll open any of the old-fashioned kinds of locks. They don't work on the doors in new houses, only old houses, and especially haunted houses."

I asked Bobby if he got his key from a dead detective or a dead robber. But he said it came from his father's tool chest. He said he didn't know where his father got it. He said that he had already tried it out on the door to the old Conolly place and it worked fine.

Of course, I didn't really believe the Conolly place was haunted. It's just a run-down old house near the edge of town. My dad says it's an eyesore. All the bushes have grown up tall along a rickety picket fence and the yard is full of blackberry vines. I'd never heard of anybody who'd really seen a ghost there. It just looked spooky at night, that's all.

The idea of going in a haunted house was kind of scary, though, so we said we'd do it. Bobby had to go home and get his skeleton key and, since it was almost time for supper, we agreed to meet in the bushes behind the Conolly house after we'd eaten. Melvin said we should hurry so that we could go in the house and get back out while there was still daylight.

Me and Melvin were finished supper and waiting in the backyard of the old house within half an hour. But Bobby didn't show up until almost dark. Melvin was pretty nervous by that time and I thought he might chicken out on us. But he never said anything about it so we all snuck around to the front porch.

Bobby's skeleton key looked just about like any other old-fashioned kind of key. I was glad when it opened the door on the first try. I didn't want any of the neighbours to see us messing around there. I was afraid they might call our parents or something. We weren't going to hurt anything, but we weren't supposed to be there either.

Inside, the empty house smelled like dust and dirty socks. The sun was mostly down so everything looked shadowy, spookier than it would have in daylight. The walls were yellowed, and cobwebs seemed to be everywhere.

The house had two big rooms on the main floor, plus a kitchen in the back, and a little tiny room at the bottom of the staircase. Upstairs, there were three small bedrooms and a hallway that led to an attic. The attic had a sloping ceiling with nails poking through from the outside. A window at the far end opened onto a roof over the back porch.

Even with the window, the attic was darker than the rest of the house. An old kitchen chair was knocked over in the middle of the room and boxes were stacked along the walls. Most of them were filled with papers, but one of them had a bunch of clothes in it.

I was still looking through the boxes when Bobby went over to the window and opened it. It wasn't locked or anything. The sky was almost dark. A big old mulberry tree was growing close to the house. I looked past it and could see all the way to the playground behind the school.

"This must be the place where he did it," Bobby said. "This attic must be where old Ben Conolly hanged himself."

I didn't know what Bobby was talking about. People called the house the Conolly place, and of course everybody said it was haunted, all the kids anyway. But I'd never heard anything about anybody named Ben Conolly. And I sure didn't know anything about anybody hanging themselves.

"I'll bet that's the chair he stood on to do it," Bobby said. "I'll bet that's why they never took it away with the rest of the furniture. They probably just left that old chair here with the rope because they were scared to touch it."

"What are you talking about?" Melvin said. "There isn't any rope in here. Nobody hanged himself."

"Do you wanna bet?" Bobby said. "That's why this house is empty. Because old Ben Conolly hanged himself here and nobody has been able to live in it ever since. It's haunted by his ghost."

Melvin asked Bobby how he knew that, but I didn't wait around to hear the answer. I didn't know if I believed Bobby or not, but I did know I wanted out of that house. It had been spooky enough before, but after Bobby said that about Ben Conolly, it was way too spooky for me.

At first, I thought I'd just climb through the window onto the roof and shimmy down the mulberry tree. That way, I could get out without going back through the house. But I figured if I did that I'd probably slip in the dark and fall. Besides, Bobby would have laughed at me for sure.

I started down the stairs. By this time, everything was pitch black. I couldn't even make out the flowers I'd seen on the wallpaper on my way up. Bobby and Melvin were coming down the stairs behind me. I could hear Melvin saying, "Nobody hanged himself here. You just made that up."

Once we got back outside, we tore away as fast as we could run. We didn't stop until we got to Third Street, near where Bobby lived. The last thing Bobby said to us as he headed up the street towards his place was that we should go back to the house some night at twelve o'clock. Then we'd be sure to see a ghost.

I didn't figure we'd ever go back, but the next morning, Melvin came over before I'd even finished breakfast. He was still all excited about the Conolly house. "There isn't anybody who hanged himself in there," he said. "My dad says he thinks the reason they call it the Conolly house is that somebody named Conolly from another town owns it. But it's not Ben Conolly. He says he never even heard of anybody named Ben Conolly."

4

It didn't take long to find out the real reason Melvin was so excited. He had an idea for getting back at Bobby for all the times Bobby had teased him. "I've got a plan," Melvin said. "We'll get Bobby to go in the old Conolly house and then we'll sneak in and scare him. We'll make him think he saw the ghost of Ben Conolly."

I didn't know about scaring Bobby, but I knew it would be easy enough to get him to go in that house. "We'll go camping," I said. "Then, we'll dare Bobby to go in there at midnight. That's when he said there'd be ghosts. Then we'll sneak in after him."

"No," Melvin said. "We'll climb up the mulberry tree and go in the window. Bobby left it open and we can probably get to the attic before he does. We'll ambush him when he comes up the stairs."

"Wait a minute," I said. "We'll dare Bobby to sleep in the house all night by himself. Bobby always takes a dare. Then, when he's in there, we can really scare him."

Melvin grinned. "We'll see who's afraid of ghosts," he said.

Just as we figured, we had no trouble talking Bobby into sleeping all night in the Conolly house. When he said we should go back at midnight, Melvin just laughed. He said that going in that old house at midnight wouldn't do any good.

"If you want to see a real ghost," Melvin told Bobby, "what you have to do is go to a cemetery at night. Go to the last grave and walk around it backwards twelve times. That's to raise the dead. Then go to a haunted house and sleep in it. If there are ghosts, you'll see them before the sun comes up."

Even Bobby looked a little pale when Melvin told him about walking twelve times, backwards, around a grave. He was trapped, though. He was the one who wanted to see a ghost. When Melvin said he was too scared to do it, Bobby had to say he wasn't scared at all.

That night, we arranged to go camping down by the creek in the park at the edge of town. We camp there a lot in the summer. My dad even sets up his big tent for us.

5

When it began to get dark, we walked up River Road to the cemetery. Bobby was nervous. I could tell because he wasn't saying much. It wasn't like when he climbed the water tower.

We all went together as far as the cemetery gate. After that, Bobby had to go on alone. "You have to walk all the way through to the other side," Melvin said. "When you get to the last tombstone, walk around it backwards twelve times. We'll be waiting just outside the fence. Remember, you have to go twelve times around the grave. We'll count and make sure you don't miss any."

Melvin and I ran all the way around the outside of the cemetery. But when we got to the other side, Bobby was already there waiting for us. He was outside the fence, too. Melvin said there hadn't been enough time for Bobby to have walked around the last grave twelve times, backwards. But Bobby said he did. He also said he wanted to get out of there. "Cemeteries give me the creeps," he said.

Bobby didn't talk all the way to the Conolly house. When we got there he opened the door with his skeleton key. I gave him the sleeping bag I'd been carrying. "Well, look out for ghosts," I said.

Melvin asked Bobby if he was scared yet. But Bobby just shook his head and went inside. "See you," I said as the door closed behind him. I knew I wouldn't have tried sleeping in that house even if I knew for sure there weren't any ghosts in it. Even if I had proof from the government or something.

Melvin and I walked back to the street. We waited a couple of minutes, then cut down the alley into the backyard by the mulberry tree. I went up the tree first. Melvin came right behind me. The window was still open and we climbed inside.

We had planned to cover ourselves with clothes from the box in the attic and then go spooking around the house until Bobby got scared and ran away. But when we got in there the house was even darker than it had been the last time we were there. I couldn't see the boxes, the chair, or anything. "Sheesh," Melvin said, "we should have brought a flashlight."

After a minute, my eyes began to adjust to the dark. I still couldn't see much, but some light was coming through the doorway from the hall outside the attic. I could see the shadow the chair made in the middle of the room. "See if you can find that box of clothes," I whispered to Melvin. "I'm going to go make some noises on the stairway."

The hall was nearly as dark as the attic. Just the sliver of a new moon cast its light through the window. I couldn't see much, only the shadows a step or two ahead of me. I could hear Melvin moving boxes around in the room behind me.

All at once, there was a loud thud on the stairway. Then, footsteps. Before I could move, a shape appeared in the hall in front of me. I didn't scream, at least not out loud. But inside my head I did.

I don't even remember when I started to run. I just remember tripping over the chair in the middle of the attic, and then being on the roof and climbing down the tree. Melvin kept stepping on my fingers, trying to get down ahead of me. When we hit the ground we were already running.

As we ran, though, I could hear laughter coming from the house behind us. That's when I guessed what the shape on the stairs must have been. Somehow, Bobby had known we were in there. Instead of us scaring him, he had scared us.

When Melvin and I got back to the tent, we couldn't believe it—Bobby was already there. He told us he hadn't been able to sleep in the house. He said that he heard noises in the attic. He said he couldn't stand to stay there. He said he didn't think anybody would be able to sleep in that house. When Bobby told us that, I didn't know what to say.

I still figure it was Bobby who scared us, but a couple of things bother me about it. Maybe he could have beat us back to our camp if he had run all the way. But why didn't he tease us about it? And who did we hear laughing?

And what really gives me the willies is something Bobby said later that night. The fire had died down and we were lying in our sleeping bags in the tent. Bobby kept talking about all of the noises he had heard. Then he said that when he walked around that grave in the cemetery — backwards, twelve times — he said he looked down at the tombstone, and it was Ben Conolly's grave.

Tom Sawyer's Ghost

The boy Mark Twain wrote about in the book The Adventures of Tom Sawyer *lived a hundred and fifty years ago. While today's readers can still admire Tom's irrepressive spirit, only a few, like Robbie, ever get a chance to go along with Tom on one of his adventures.*

Spring came early that year. The winter had been mild. By March, the snow had melted. Water in the creek was high, although not as high as usual in spring. By the middle of the month, farmers were already working the land. People in town were spading their gardens.

On the afternoon of the twenty-first, the first official day of spring, Robbie Matthews sat in the classroom. Mr. Dingus, the teacher, was explaining the intricacies of dividing with fractions. Robbie's attention was outside the room, however. His head faced forward, towards the blackboard. But his eyes gazed to the right, across three rows of seats, out the window to the schoolyard, and beyond to the trees and river in the distance.

In most places, the river was only three or four feet deep, even in spring. At its widest it was, perhaps, thirty feet across. At one spot, just past the bridge, it was so narrow that Robbie's friend Alan Bender could spit all the way to the other side. Of course, Alan could spit farther than anyone Robbie knew. Spitting was his main talent.

The river didn't have a name, or if it did, nobody in town ever used it. Robbie had never heard anyone call it anything but "the crick." He had no knowledge of the river's headwaters, and only a vague notion of how, some miles to the south, it joined a larger river that ran north and then west into Lake Michigan.

The part of the river that flowed for a few miles on either side of Maple Valley, though, Robbie knew everything about. He had explored each twist and tributary for several miles upriver. He and his friends had hiked along its bank for just as many miles downstream. Their river was small, but it provided the boys with as much adventure as if it had been the Mississippi itself.

About a mile south of town, they had built a hut, a small board cabin with a tarpaper roof and no window. It was on a point of land where a smaller stream added its waters to Robbie's river. Once, an empty, old, leaky, flat-bottomed boat, loose in the river, had floated by the hut. The boys had waded out and climbed aboard. They rode the boat all the way to Baldur, the next town south, seven miles away in Indiana.

Mr. Dingus was explaining contour plowing now. Robbie had missed the moment when his teacher had stopped talking about arithmetic and started talking about geography. He looked at the clock. One minute before two. Only eleven minutes until recess.

Just then, Robbie saw that John Berton was writing in his workbook. So were Stevie Eldredge and Ellen Kenny. So was everyone else. Robbie's discovery came too late. Mr. Dingus had already noticed him. "Robbie," he said, "where's your geography workbook?"

Robbie began sorting quickly through the debris in his desk. "I was just getting it," he said. "I've got it right here." He opened the book and began filling in answers as best he could.

After what seemed an insufferable amount of time, Robbie looked at the clock. Three minutes after two. He thought about Tom Sawyer, the boy in the book he had just finished reading for the third time in two years.

Robbie wished he could skip school as often as Tom. He couldn't, though. When he skipped school somebody always told his dad. Robbie's dad worked in the bank so he talked to just about everybody in town every day.

Even if his dad hadn't worked in the bank, Robbie's folks would have still found out. Maple Valley was too small for anybody to skip school without getting caught. Maple Valley was too small to get away with anything. Even Tom Sawyer would have had trouble in Maple Valley.

How could time move so slowly? Six minutes after two. Robbie began writing in his workbook again, but at the same time, he kept an eye on Mr. Dingus. If the opportunity presented itself, he would throw a paper wad at Alan Bender. He looked at the clock repeatedly. Seven minutes after two. Then eight. Then nine. At last, after one more agonizingly long minute, the recess bell finally rang.

Outside, Robbie and John shot a few games of marbles with Kevin Hawkins. Afterwards, they sat on the school steps to watch the river and admire the spring morning. Only a few clouds, wispy like chimney smoke, shared the sky with the sun. Alan Bender came over and sat down beside them. "It feels like summer," Alan said. "It's hot as summer already."

"I'll bet the water in the crick is warm enough to swim in," said Kevin.

"Let's go then," said Robbie. "Let's skip school for the rest of the day and go swimming."

"You're nuts," said Alan. "If we don't come in after recess Old Dingus will have a search party out after us before we even have a chance to get used to the water. And if Dingus ever caught us skipping school, we wouldn't get outside again until summer vacation."

"Come on," said Robbie. "You think Tom Sawyer would let Old Dingus keep him from skipping school?"

Just then, the bell on the brick building behind them signalled that recess had ended. The boys got up slowly. "We might as well go in, Robbie," John said. "The water in the crick's probably too cold for swimming yet anyway."

Robbie lagged behind the other boys. He wished he could run away into the woods with Tom Sawyer. Tom

11

would never let Old Dingus get the best of him. He wouldn't be afraid to skip school and go swimming.

Back inside, the boys took their seats. Mr. Dingus began diagramming sentences on the blackboard. He wrote a sentence and asked the class what its subject was. Ellen Kenny raised her hand.

Robbie looked at the clock. Twenty-five minutes before three. Nearly an hour before school would let out. Mr. Dingus asked John Berton what adjective modified the sentence's subject. Robbie looked at the blackboard, then let his eyes drift back across the room to the window and the river beyond. He glanced up at the clock. Twenty-two minutes before three.

He looked again at the blackboard. Mr. Dingus was diagramming another sentence. Robbie closed and opened his eyes. Then he put his elbows on his desk and let his head rest in his hands. The chalk squeaked with each word Mr. Dingus wrote.

Robbie rubbed his eyes and watched the teacher diagram three more sentences. Not once did he attempt to understand the mysterious concepts Mr. Dingus explained so intently. Each time Robbie looked at the clock he was discouraged to see how little time had passed.

He looked at the back of Alan Bender's head, examining a swirl of hair that poked up in the air in defiance of Alan's comb. Robbie wished he had skipped school. He wished he had gone swimming. Mr. Dingus turned to write another sentence on the blackboard. Robbie closed his eyes.

"Pssst," he heard a voice behind him say. Robbie turned and saw a smiling boy with straw-coloured hair. "Let's go," said the boy. "Let's get out of here while Old Dingus has his back turned."

Robbie looked around at his teacher. Mr. Dingus was still writing the sentence on the blackboard. Without another word he slid from his seat and slipped out the classroom door with the boy. Once outside, they snuck along the edge of the building until they were past the window. Then they made a break for it, running across the playground to the trees near the river.

Only when they reached the water did they stop running and begin to laugh. They laughed and danced up and down and slapped each other on the back. "We made it," Robbie said. "I'll bet Old Dingus hasn't even noticed we're gone."

"If he has," said the other boy, "it's too late now. We're free. Now we can swim. Afterwards, we'll get Huck and Joe and run off to be pirates."

Robbie looked closely at the boy. "Why, you're Tom," he said. "You're Tom Sawyer."

"Who'd you think I was," said the boy. "Huckleberry Finn?"

Robbie showed Tom the way to the swimming hole. Quickly, they stripped off their clothes and waded into the river. Even though it was still March, the water was warmer than Robbie could ever remember it. The boys swam until they were tired. Then they dried in the sun on the riverbank.

When they finally got dressed again, Robbie showed Tom the hut he and his friends had built. Inside, Tom climbed up and sat on the top bunk of the two built-in beds. He seemed impressed with the hut.

"We could be robbers," he said, "and this could be our hide-out. We'd make our escapes in boats. That way, not even bloodhounds would be able to follow our tracks. And if someone discovered our hide-out, we'd cut out his tongue so he wouldn't be able to tell anybody we were here."

Robbie smiled, even though he didn't know what to think of the idea of cutting out somebody's tongue. "Who will we rob?" he asked.

"Oh, we won't rob people, only banks and stage-coaches. And steamboats, maybe. Steamboats always carry lots of silver and gold. And sometimes jewels."

"You won't find too many stagecoaches and steamboats around here," said Robbie. "In fact, you won't find any. And as for banks, there's only one in this town and my dad runs it."

Robbie saw that this information disturbed Tom. He evidently couldn't imagine a place without stagecoaches and steamboats. And only one bank. Tom didn't say anything for some time. Finally, he allowed that it was no good being robbers in Maple Valley.

"We could get along without steamboats," Tom said. "Or even stagecoaches. But there's no point to being robbers without a good supply of banks. Banks are the main things to rob. Stagecoaches and steamboats are just extras. They're for when you get tired of robbing banks and want to do something different."

Tom jumped down from the bunk and walked outside. Robbie followed. "I'll tell you what," Tom said when they got to the riverbank. "Instead of robbers, let's be adventurers. Being adventurers is a lot better than being robbers anyway. We can build a raft and float down the river. We can go clear to the Mississippi. Maybe all the way around the world."

Robbie thought that idea sounded swell. "But what do adventurers do?" he asked.

"Adventurers don't really do anything," said Tom. "They just travel about, climbing mountains and discovering new countries. Sometimes they save people when there's a call for it, but that's about all. Except go to big dinners, of course. Everybody's always giving big dinners to honour adventurers. They give them awards and medals and such like. Sometimes money, too. But adventurers usually give the money away to somebody else who needs it more."

In no time at all, Robbie and Tom had built a raft. They made it from three short logs and some of the leftover lumber from the cabin. Tom took an axe and cut two maple saplings so they could pole the raft away from shore and around tight spots in the river.

Then they were off. At first Robbie stood and poled the raft to keep it drifting in the centre of the river. Tom sat at the front of the craft telling stories about some of his past adventures. After a while both boys lay back and let the current carry them. The sun was still warm, although

Robbie thought it must have been getting late in the afternoon by then.

Tom told about the time he and Huck had seen Indian Joe murder Doctor Robinson. He told about going to his own funeral and the time he and Becky Thatcher had been lost in the cave. Then he explained to Robbie how to cure warts with spunk water and how to tie strings on dead rats so that they wouldn't come off when you swung them around your head.

Robbie sat back and listened with his eyes closed. He felt the warm sun on his face. It was the best day of his life. He thought of poor Alan and John stuck back in the schoolroom with Mr. Dingus. He thought how jealous they would be if they could see him now. The river grew wider as they travelled south. Skiffs and other rafts occasionally passed by.

Then, as they rounded a curve in the river, a steamboat appeared. She was too far off to read her name, but Robbie could see the paddle wheel churning up water. Then she blew her whistle and Robbie heard the bell ring. He looked up from his desk, blinked his eyes, and saw that the hands on the clock said three-thirty.

Robbie's classmates were already filing out the door on their way home. Mr. Dingus stood in front of the blackboard. "Well, Robbie," he said. "Have you learned anything at all today?"

"I guess I learned a little," Robbie said. Then he remembered the spunk water for curing warts and how to tie strings to dead rats. He remembered all he had learned with Tom Sawyer.

"Actually, I learned quite a lot today," he told his teacher. "Way more than usual."

The Ghost Who Came
at Christmas

Uncle Charlie was Sherri's favourite uncle. He knew all sorts of games and he told stories better than anybody. Sherri never knew if she should believe the stories, but they always made her laugh.

Sherri McMichaels liked everything about Christmas. She liked the way people smiled and said, "Merry Christmas." She liked decorating the Christmas tree. She liked the way the house smelled on Christmas Day, with turkey and pies and sweet potatoes baking in the oven. At Christmas, she even liked her younger brother Harold.

Another thing Sherri McMichaels liked about Christmas was that her Uncle Charlie always came to visit. Uncle Charlie was her mother's brother, and Sherri's favourite uncle. Maybe even Sherri's favourite person in the whole world. Every Christmas he arrived just before supper and stayed until the next afternoon. Then he'd return to his farm. It was more than a hundred miles away so Uncle Charlie didn't visit often.

As far as Sherri and Harold were concerned, Uncle Charlie was more fun than any adult they knew. He played just as much as they did with the toys they got for Christmas. He made up games they would never have thought of on their own.

Best of all, he told them stories. He told them stories about places he had been and things he had done. They were real stories that had happened to him when he was a sailor, not the fairy tale kind of stories their teachers told—although Sherri's father sometimes grumbled that Uncle Charlie's stories sounded like fairy tales to him.

Uncle Charlie made Christmas so much fun, Sherri and Harold hated to go to bed on Christmas night even more than other nights. One year, when they had been told twice that it was past bedtime, Sherri said, "But, Mom, we can't go to bed yet. Uncle Charlie hasn't told us a story."

"Well, maybe there's time for just one story," Sherri's mother said. "But afterwards, you have to go straight to bed."

"After Charlie tells a story, we'll probably all be ready for bed," said Sherri's father.

"What kind of story will it be, Uncle Charlie?" asked Harold sitting down on the couch beside his uncle. Sherri was already sitting next to him on the other side. "Will it be about when you were a sailor?"

"No," said Uncle Charlie. "This story is about some-thing that happened just recently. The truth is, a couple of months ago I saw a ghost."

"A ghost," said Sherri. "What did you do?"

"What did I do?" said Uncle Charlie. "There wasn't anything I could do except try to get away. When you see a ghost you don't invite it to dinner or even ask it to come home with you. When you see a ghost, the natural tendency is to run.

"The way it happened, I had been over to see my old friend Albert Williams. I just meant to stop by his house for a short visit. But, of course, we got to talking and the time slipped away from us. The next thing I knew it was almost midnight. Past when I should have been home in bed.

"Now, as you probably remember, there's an old cemetery between the Williams farm and mine. As I was driving home, my pickup truck ran out of gas just before I got to the cemetery gate. It didn't bother me too much that I had to walk home. It was only a couple of miles and I've walked by that old graveyard a hundred times after dark. I'd never seen any ghosts or spirits or spooks of any kind out there. But on this night, things turned out different.

"I was hoofing it for home when I got an idea to take a short cut through the cemetery. I planned to just nip across one corner of the graveyard and then climb the fence into Dave Jenkins's pasture. Cutting across there would take a quarter mile or so off my walk. About half-way through the cemetery, though, I tripped over something and fell on my face.

"I skinned up my leg pretty awful, too. It stung like the blazes where I'd banged into whatever I'd tripped over. It felt like it was bleeding. I got up and dusted myself off, and that's when I saw a man standing just a few feet away from me.

"He startled me so much I darned near fell back over again. But the man said hello just as calm as if there were nothing in the world unusual about being alone at night in the middle of a graveyard. 'Nice fall weather we've been having lately,' he said.

"I was just about to tell him that we could use an inch or two more rain when I saw that he had his head, or at least somebody's head, tucked underneath his arm like a garden cabbage. 'Mister,' said the ghost, 'would you put that back for me?'

"Well, when I saw that head, and heard what the ghost said, I didn't wait around for any more talk about the weather. I ran away so fast I was a mile down the road before I took my next breath.

"When I looked back over my shoulder, though, there was that ghost running right along only a couple of steps behind me."

"Did he still have his head under his arm?" asked Harold.

"He sure did," said Uncle Charlie.

"Wait a minute," said Sherri's father looking up from the book Aunt Mildred had given him for Christmas. "If he had his head under his arm, how did he talk?"

"I'd give the world to know," said Uncle Charlie. "If he was dead I didn't understand how he could run either, but he did. In fact, he kept chasing me right by the front door of my house. He was right on my heels so I couldn't stop. I ran along like that for three miles with that ghost no more than a step or two behind me the whole way.

"Finally, I just couldn't run anymore. I was tired and out of breath. I'd plumb run out of steam so I sat down on a log at the side of the road. The ghost, he stopped running too, and sat down beside me."

"Was his head still under his arm?" asked Harold.

"Yes," said Uncle Charlie. "He was worn-out and breathing hard, but he still had his head. After a minute, he turned to me just as calm as you please and said, 'We've had a nice run.'"

"Did the ghost say that you'd had a nice run or did the head?" asked Sherri's father.

"Oh, the ghost said it all right," said Uncle Charlie. "You could see an image of his face in the air above his shoulders. The head could have said it, too. But I wasn't watchin' the head. I couldn't stand to look at it."

"What did you say?" asked Sherri.

"What did I say? I agreed with him. I said we'd had a fine run. I also said that we were going to have another fine run just as soon as I could catch my breath.

"Then the ghost told me he wanted me to put it back for him before we ran any more, and when I heard that I took off running again. I figured that head was his responsibility. When I looked back, though, there was that ghost running right along behind me."

"Wait a minute," said Sherri's father. "I thought you said you'd hurt your leg."

"I did hurt my leg," said Uncle Charlie. "Why that leg hurt so bad I could barely keep running. But I was too scared to stop. We ran for seven more miles. I was so tired and my leg hurt so much I figured I'd have to stop. But every time I looked back and saw that ghost running along behind me, why I just ran some more. Finally, I couldn't stand it any longer. I had to stop to rest."

"Did the ghost stop, too?" Harold asked.

"He sure did," said Uncle Charlie, "and the first thing he said was that he wanted me to put it back."

"What did you say?" asked Harold.

"Well, I told him I didn't know how to put it back. I wasn't no doctor. I said that it wasn't my fault it got knocked off in the first place."

"What did the ghost say?"

"Why, he said that it was my fault. He said it was me that knocked it over. And he said that if I knocked it over, it was my job to put it back up."

"Do you mean you fell over the ghost and knocked his head off?" asked Sherri.

"Well that's what I asked the ghost," said Uncle Charlie. "And it turned out I hadn't knocked off his head at all. I'd tripped over his tombstone. That's why he came out of the grave. I had knocked over his tombstone and he wanted me to fix it. He said that ever since he'd been dead he hadn't been able to lift anything heavy.

"After that, we got to talking and he didn't seem like such a bad ghost and . . . Well, to make a long story short, we walked back to the graveyard. I lifted his tombstone back up like it's supposed to be. Then, I walked the rest of the way home and that ended that."

"Did you see the ghost go back in the ground?" asked Harold.

"No," said Uncle Charlie. "He just kind of floated up into the air. But before he left, he told me that any time I went away from home, he'd come along and look after me so I wouldn't get into any kind of trouble. He said he'd protect me."

"Do you see him again every time you leave home?" asked Sherri.

"No," said Uncle Charlie. "I haven't seen him since that night at the graveyard. But he told me that if I'd listen carefully, sometimes at night, whenever I was away from home I'd hear a "whooo" like a hoot owl makes. Only it wouldn't sound just like a hoot owl. It'd be a little different, and that noise would be him."

"Wait a minute," said Sherri's dad. "What happened to the ghost's head? If you didn't knock it off, why was he carrying it around with him like that?"

21

"I never did find out," said Uncle Charlie. "I wanted to know, but it just didn't seem polite to ask him. I figured if he wanted to carry his head around under his arm, it was his business."

"Time for bed now," said Sherri's mother. "You've had your story."

A few minutes later, while Sherri's father was tucking her in bed for the night, he asked if her Christmas had been a good one.

"Oh yes," she said. "But, Dad, do you believe the story Uncle Charlie told about the ghost?"

"No," said her father. "There are no such things as ghosts."

Just then, Sherri heard a sound from outside her window. It was like an owl. But she thought it might not be exactly like an owl. Her father turned towards the window but then stopped and quickly looked back at her.

Sherri smiled and said good night.

The Bus to Winnipeg

Michael didn't want to move. He wanted to stay in Sault Ste. Marie with his friends. It was only after meeting another passenger on the bus to Winnipeg that he began to feel fortunate.

"At least I get to sit by myself," Michael thought as he took his seat. The bus was nearly full and since there weren't three empty seats together he had been allowed to sit alone. He chose one of the two vacant seats at the very back, across the aisle from the bathroom. His mother and younger brother, Andy, sat near the front.

Michael didn't want to be on the bus in the first place. To have had to sit with his mother and little brother all the way to Winnipeg would have made the trip even worse. Before the bus had pulled away from the station in Sault Ste. Marie he could hear his mother scolding Andy for picking his nose. Michael didn't know who was more embarrassing, his nagging mother or snotty-nosed little brother.

Michael didn't want to move to Winnipeg. He wanted to stay in The Sault where he had friends, where he could keep playing on his own hockey team, where he had lived all twelve years of his life. As the bus maneuvered through the narrow downtown streets Michael stared through his window at the snowbanks piled higher than the cars. He wondered if the snowbanks were as high in Winnipeg.

Soon, the bus left the town, speeding along the highway

23

going north and west around Lake Superior. The fading evening light turned into darkness and the view from Michael's window became a reflection of himself. Sometimes, the bus passed by houses next to the highway. Occasionally, it passed, without stopping, through tiny villages. A flash of lights would whiz through the image on the window, and Michael would strain unsuccessfully to see beyond it.

Three times the bus stopped in small northern towns along the lake. Other passengers got off to stretch their legs and eat hamburgers and potato chips. Twice Michael's mother and brother got off, too. But Michael stayed on the bus. He knew his mother wouldn't buy anything to eat. She was saving money. She had a lunch packed that was supposed to last them through the night until the next morning when they would get to their new home.

When the bus stopped at Nipigon only a few people got off. It was nearly midnight and many of the passengers were sleeping in their seats. Michael could see his mother, but his brother was out of sight in the seat beside her.

Michael leaned his head against the window and looked at his reflection in the glass. He watched the people standing in the cold outside the bus. He watched their frosty breath floating in the icy air. He looked at the Christmas lights in the windows of the stores.

Michael was nearly asleep when the driver returned. He closed his eyes so he only felt the bus as it inched forward up the hill out of town, gradually regaining speed on the highway to Thunder Bay.

He didn't even notice when the other boy sat down beside him. But after a few minutes, he realized someone was there. He opened his eyes. He couldn't see anyone's reflection beside his own in the window. Somehow, though, he knew someone was in the next seat.

"Hello," a boy in a red toque said when Michael turned. "I didn't think anyone was sitting here so I sat down." He held out his hand. "My name's Kevin," he said.

The boys shook hands and Michael told his new seatmate his name. The boy's hand was cold so Michael guessed he had just got on the bus. "I didn't see you before," he said. "You must have got on at that last town."

The boy shook his head. "I've been on this bus all day," he said. "I've been in Toronto visiting my father. I'm going home to Winnipeg."

"I'm going to Winnipeg, too," said Michael. "Only it's not my home. Not yet anyway. We're moving. My dad got a new job. He's been in Winnipeg for a month. It took him this long to find us a new house."

"You're lucky. My dad got transferred to Toronto. Only he never did find us a house. My parents ended up getting a divorce instead. Now I go to Toronto to visit him on holidays and in the summer. My mom used to take me, but I've been back and forth so many times she says I can do it myself now. It's only a day and a night on the bus you know."

"You go by yourself? How old are you?"

"Thirteen. How old are you?"

"Almost thirteen."

"I'm almost fourteen. You'll probably go by yourself next year, too. Only your dad lives in Winnipeg so you won't have to."

"Maybe I'll go back to The Sault and visit some of my friends."

"Maybe. But you'll like Winnipeg. There's lots to do there. I'd just as soon stay home for my holidays. But my dad wants me in Toronto so I have to go back and forth all the time. I was there for Christmas. Now I'm going home to have another Christmas with my mom."

"It must be fun getting to ride the bus by yourself."

"It's all right. But I want to go home. Last time there was an accident."

"What happened?"

"I figured you would have heard about it. But look. It's snowing again."

Michael looked up to see snow pelting against the bus's windshield. The wipers swung back and forth, scraping ice and snow in both directions across the window. From

25

the back of the dark bus it looked as if they were in outer space. The snow was a meteor shower flying past them as they sped along. "How can the driver see?" Michael asked.

"I don't believe he can," said the boy. At that moment, the bus slowed. Michael saw lights ahead on the highway. At first, he only saw headlights and the steady blinking of a light from a police car. But then, as the bus passed the scene in the night, he saw that there had been an accident.

He turned to look out the rear window. A transport truck and a Greyhound bus were lying in the ditch at the side of the road. An ambulance and police car were parked at the edge of the highway. Michael watched until he couldn't see anything anymore. When he turned around, the boy who had been with him had disappeared.

Michael looked along the darkened rows of seats, trying to see where the boy had gone. But he couldn't find him in the shadows of sleeping passengers. He turned to look back at the accident, but he could see only darkness. He leaned his forehead against the window. His entire bus ride seemed like a dream. His mother and brother. Winnipeg. Sault Ste. Marie. The boy in the red toque.

In a few minutes, the bus pulled into the station in Thunder Bay. The driver announced a thirty-minute rest stop. Michael decided to get off and find the other boy. His mother stood up by her seat and waved to him.

"Michael," she said when he got closer, "we're going to go in and have a hot chocolate or something warm to drink. What do you think?"

An hour before, Michael would have found the idea of drinking a hot chocolate with his mother and little brother objectionable. Somehow, though, in the middle of the night in Thunder Bay, it seemed all right. He'd even invite the boy in the red toque to join them.

Michael didn't see the boy in the restaurant, though. And when he asked his mother about the wreck on the highway, she said she hadn't seen one. Michael couldn't believe she had missed it. When the waitress arrived with their hot chocolate, he asked her if she had heard about a bus accident close to town.

"You must mean the bus that collided with the transport truck," said the waitress. "It was in a snow storm."

"That's right," said Michael. "The truck and bus both ended up in the ditch."

"That was a bad accident," said the waitress. "Lots of people were hurt. A boy from Winnipeg was killed. It happened three years ago, just about this time of year."

"Three years ago?" Michael said.

"That's right," said the waitress. "It'd be just about three years ago exactly. I was working the graveyard shift that night, too. The bus from Toronto was late and then the police came in and told us what happened.

"I knew that little boy. I recognized his picture in the paper. I remember him because he came through here just before Christmas. He was on his way to Toronto to see his father, riding all that way by himself. I remember he was wearing a red toque."

Michael sat quietly, barely touching his cocoa until it was time to leave. Back on the bus, he sat, awake, riding through the night. Riding towards Winnipeg. Watching his reflection in the window. Somewhere near the Manitoba border, just as the sun was coming up, he looked down and, for a moment, he thought he saw a crumpled, red toque on the seat beside him.

Lost in the Snow

Few scientists believe in ghosts. But for the scientist who tells this story, admitting the existence of a ghost seems the only way to explain what happened.

I'm a scientist. I've worked in a chemistry lab for nearly forty years. I'm not the kind of person who believes in ghosts. But the truth is, I saw a ghost once when I was a young man. The ghost even saved my life.

I grew up on a farm in the country. I had to walk two and a half miles to a one-room country school. In the winter, when the snow was deep, or the weather particularly cold, my brothers and I rode in a cutter pulled by an old horse named Bell.

I was only seven or eight years old when I found Blackie. He was just a pup, part border collie and part something else. Because of his colour, we always figured he had some Labrador retriever in him. I found him in a snowstorm on my way home from school.

When my brothers and I had left the house that morning it was a pleasant winter day, but it started snowing about noon. By the time school let out there must have been a foot of new snow on the ground.

I trudged after my older brothers, Jim and Tom, trying to keep up on the way home. But the drifts were so thick I fell behind almost before we left the schoolyard. By the time I'd walked the mile and a half cross-country to our road, my two brothers were completely out of sight.

It had stopped snowing. I had just come up onto the

road, following in Jim and Tom's tracks, when I first saw Blackie. He was in a snowdrift a few yards back, down at the corner where we turned to go to town.

He let out a little yelp when he saw me, as if to say that it was my fault he was there. It was a desperate, tired puppy-bark, filled with fear, but hope too. It was to let me know that taking care of him was my responsibility.

I never learned where he came from or how he got there, but he wouldn't have been able to go much farther by himself in that snow. I carried him home and put him in an old hog shed attached to the barn. Dad never believed in dogs coming into the house. At first, Dad wasn't even going to let me keep Blackie, but he changed his mind when he saw the pup had some collie in him. He thought Blackie might make a good cattle dog.

I guess every kid has a dog that's special to him. Growing up in the country, though—where there's so much to do outside and not many other children around to do things with—just naturally brings a boy and dog closer together.

Blackie turned out to be an okay cattle dog, although never good enough to suit Dad. Mostly, he was just my dog. Even though I was the youngest one in the family, I became his master. We'd hunt gophers in the summer and rabbits in the winter. Blackie never went with my older brothers unless I was along. Everybody said it was because he knew I had taken him in and saved him from the snowstorm.

I spent more time with Blackie when I was a kid than I did with my brothers. They were four and five years older than I was. By the time I was twelve, they were already out of school, working full-time on the farm. Blackie was my real companion. Except at night when he slept in the shed by the barn, or while I was in school, we were always together.

In the winter, Blackie would leave for school with me every morning, but he'd only go as far as the corner where I had first found him. That's where I'd leave the road to cut across Casey's Meadow and hike along the creek to the school. Blackie would go back to the house then. But he'd always be waiting for me at the corner again when I'd come home in the afternoon.

All through school, it was the same. There wasn't a day when Blackie wasn't there in the afternoon to greet me. Even during my last three years in high school when I had to live in town with my grandparents four nights a week, Blackie would still be waiting for me at the corner when Mr. Haskins left me off on his way home from his job with the railroad.

After I graduated from high school, I was lucky enough to get a scholarship to go to the University of Toronto. Blackie was getting old by then, but we still hiked the fields and woods around home during the summer when I came back to work on the farm with my brothers.

Blackie was thirteen years old the last summer I was home. His heart was bad and he couldn't romp across the fields the way he had before. But he still followed me around the barnyard and we took short walks down the road. Once, we even went as far as the corner where we'd walked so many times when we were younger. The summer heat was too much for the old dog, though, and I ended up having to carry him home.

After that, Blackie seemed slower than ever. He rarely ventured very far from the hog shed where he had slept every night since I'd first brought him home. When it came time for me to go back to school in the fall, I suspected it was the last time I'd ever see my boyhood companion. I didn't plan on being home again for a year, and I knew Blackie wouldn't be able to live that long.

At Christmas, though, school let out sooner than usual for the holidays, and the medical lab where I had been working part-time for two years said they wouldn't need me back until after the New Year's holiday. I decided to go home and celebrate the first Christmas with my family in four years.

It would take three and a half days to get there, and the ticket was more than I could afford. But I knew I should go anyway. I would surprise everyone. The train arrived

31

in my home town late in the afternoon on Christmas Eve. It was snowing, but the weather seemed mild. I could hardly wait to see the surprised faces of my family.

Since it was so late in the day, I knew Grandma and Grandpa would already be at the farm. I never even thought about looking for a ride. It was less than ten miles home and someone was bound to come along the road and give me a lift.

As I walked north out of town it began to snow somewhat heavier, and the wind began to blow. After an hour or so the sun went down. I walked along in the dark for miles, but no one else came along the road.

The snow was so thick I could only guess where I was. The fence posts, poking above the snow, were my only markers. I didn't dare leave the road to look for any of the farms along the way for fear of getting lost.

My feet began to get cold. I was wearing city shoes under my boots and only one pair of socks. Soon, I was so cold I stopped thinking about it. I stopped thinking about almost everything. I just stumbled on through the snow, watching for the corner where I had to turn to walk the last mile to the farm. But the dark and the blowing snow made everything look the same.

Then, I realized that I must have passed the corner where I should have turned. I stopped. I didn't know what to do. I couldn't go back, but if I'd already passed the corner there was no point in going on. Dazed, I stood in the night as the wind blew snow over my clothes and into my face.

Then I saw Blackie. I hadn't gone past the road after all. He was less than twenty yards ahead of me waiting at the corner where he had always waited. Snow covered his body just as it did mine, and he barked a greeting and then ran to me wagging his tail.

"Good boy," I said bending down to hug him. "How in the world did you know I was coming?"

With new energy, I almost ran the rest of the way home. Blackie bounded along the road beside me, happy to be with me again, and almost unmindful of the deep snow.

Without the summer heat, he seemed to have regained his health. Once we reached home, he darted into the old hog shed to get out of the weather.

I hurried onto the porch, banging on the door and opening it at the same time. Mom and Dad, my brothers, my grandparents, everybody was there. "How in the world did you get here on a night like this?" Dad said. "I could barely find my way to the barn to milk the cows."

"It wasn't snowing so much in town," I told everyone. "But I wouldn't have made it if it hadn't been for Blackie. He was waiting for me at the corner just like he used to. He showed me the way home."

My father's face turned white. My mother sat down on the couch. "Oh my," she gasped.

I looked at my brothers. "What is it?" I asked. "What's wrong?"

"It's Blackie," Tom answered. "He died the night after you left in September. He just lost his spirit and gave up."

Without saying another word, I turned and went back outside. Although I searched both the hog shed and the barn completely, I never found a sign of the dog who had led me home. There were still tracks in the snow. But only mine.

I suppose there's a good scientific explanation for what happened that night. Hallucination or something like that. I'm sure there's something quite reasonable to explain it all, although I've never been able to come up with anything satisfactory myself.

I live on the West Coast now, a place where it almost never snows. When it does, I remember the day I found that black pup lost in a drift. Then I remember the other storm, the one when I was lost and almost froze to death in the snow, and I know in my heart that Blackie brought me home.

Ghosts Around the Campfire

People are seldom afraid of ghosts during the day. But anyone who has ever listened to haunted tales beside a campfire at night knows it's a lot harder to be brave once the sun goes down.

The only time I ever saw a ghost was when I was a boy. I had gone camping with a couple of my friends, Eric Mallory and Gator Jones. Actually, I didn't really see the ghost. It was too dark. But I heard it all right. There was no doubt about that.

It was a lot like the time I saw the mountain lion. Or, to be more accurate, a lot like the time I almost saw the mountain lion. That was on a camping trip with Eric and Gator, too.

Both times we'd pitched camp, eaten our supper, and unrolled our sleeping bags. Then, for obscure reasons known only to small boys on camping trips, we lingered for several hours, huddled around the campfire, speaking in hushed tones, assuring ourselves that no wild animals were lurking in the darkness outside the fire's glow.

It was Gator who brought up the matter of mountain lions. He told us that his uncle—or maybe it was a friend of his uncle—had actually been eaten by a mountain lion. Just about the time this bit of information began to sink in, we heard a mountain lion roar somewhere in the darkness out towards the road.

The following day there was some controversy about whether the roar had actually come from a mountain lion or just an automobile on the highway. That night, however, there was no doubt in any of our minds that the sound we had heard was that of a mountain lion. All three of us abandoned camp immediately, tripping over pots and pans, tent ropes, poles, and each other in our escape. Fortunately, we had had the foresight to pitch our tent in my backyard so safety was close at hand.

It must have been a couple of years after that when our outdoor survival skills progressed to the point where we were able to leave the tamed, civilized world of backyard camping and hike deep into the wilderness. The particular wilderness we chose was in the pasture behind Eric Mallory's house.

We found an open area free of cow patties on a hill where we could see for some distance in three directions. The location provided us with optimum protection against surprise attacks from mountain lions. It also had the added advantage of being at the opposite end of the pasture from the Mallorys' dairy cows.

What we hadn't noticed, until just before dark, was that our campsite had a clear view of the town cemetery across the river. It wasn't until after we had pitched the tent, spread out our sleeping bags, and—just as the sun dipped below the horizon—begun roasting hot dogs that this matter came to our attention.

"Ah, nothing like a night in the woods to make a person feel good," said Eric, stabbing a hot dog with a sharpened stick. "I'd rather sleep outdoors than in a bed any time. It's healthier. And food tastes better when it's cooked outdoors. I can't stand eating hot dogs at home. They don't come out right cooked in a microwave."

"I know what you mean," said Gator, blowing out the flames that engulfed his wiener. "Some kids don't like doing this sort of thing. They're too finicky. They complain if their food gets even the tiniest bit overcooked. Or else, as soon as it gets dark out, they get so scared they want to go home. . . . Say, isn't that the cemetery just beyond that grove of trees over on the other side of the river?"

We all agreed that the place Gator was pointing to was, indeed, the town cemetery. "Now, you take that cemetery," said Gator warming to his subject. "That cemetery would get some kids thinking about ghosts and goblins. The first thing you know, why they'd be so scared they wouldn't even be able to sleep at night.

"They'd probably get to thinking about all the people who got buried alive back in the old days, back before undertakers used embalming fluid. They'd think how those people would wake up in their coffins, choking and running out of air. It used to happen all the time back before doctors could really tell for sure if a person was dead or not."

"I never heard anything about that," said Eric, putting down his hot dog.

"Oh yea," said Gator. "You know that old house next to the cemetery. About a hundred years ago a guy lived there and his wife died. After he buried her, her ghost came back and haunted him for seven nights in a row. Every night he'd see her image on the ceiling above his bed and she'd scream at him, 'Dig me up. Dig me up.'

"Finally, after a whole week of this, he went and dug her up to see what was wrong. And when he opened the casket he saw that her face was all bloody. She had pulled out her hair, too. See, she hadn't really been dead at all, just in a coma. But doctors didn't know about comas back then.

"When she woke up in her coffin she started screaming just like anybody would. She screamed and pulled at her hair and scratched at her face with her fingernails because she didn't know what she was doing. But nobody could hear her because she was six feet under the ground. Finally, the air in her coffin ran out and she suffocated to death."

"Jeeesh," said Eric. "I never knew anything about that."

"It happened a long time ago," said Gator. "Afterwards, the guy went completely bonkers because of what he'd done to his wife. He used to walk around the cemetery at night all by himself. Sometimes people would see him out

M. JONES

there sitting on her grave.

"It was just like he was a ghost even though he was alive. Lots of people saw him up there. They say that after he finally died, his spirit just stayed in the cemetery wandering around at night. He's probably over there right now. Maybe his wife, too."

The last rays of the evening's sunset had disappeared by this time. Clouds blew silently across the sky. "I don't really believe in ghosts," said Eric.

"I don't either," said Gator. "Especially that story about the murderer's ghost."

"What story is that?" Eric asked.

"Oh, you must have heard about that one," said Gator. "My dad tells me that one all the time. They say a guy murdered a bunch of people around here. They hanged him a long time ago, but his ghost still goes around killing people. They say that whenever he comes around you can see the ghosts of all the people he's killed. They're following him everywhere he goes so they can warn his next victim."

Eric suddenly jumped to his feet. "Look at that," he said. "There's something out there. I can see shadows moving." Eric pointed up the hill towards the fence. "Do you see? They're out there. I can see them. They're walking."

Eric was right. I could see something moving in the shadows, too. Gator must have seen it as well because nobody said anything. We just watched. We stared into the dark looking at the people, or what we thought must be people. They were walking single file through the night.

It was hard to tell, but it looked like a steady procession of shadows, dressed in white, marching across the darkened horizon. If they were the ghosts of the murdered people, there were an awful lot of them. I was too scared to move.

Then Eric figured it out. "False alarm, guys," he said. "It's only the cows. I guess they've decided to bed down at this end of the pasture." Everybody agreed with Eric, but we moved a bit closer to the fire just the same.

"I knew it couldn't be the murderer's ghost anyway," said Gator. "He always moans before he kills anybody."

"Why does he do that?" asked Eric.

"It's because they cut off his head after they killed him. See, this guy was such a terrible murderer that after they hanged him the government cut off his head and sent his brain to a bunch of scientists so they could figure out what made him such an evil person.

"To get even, the murderer's ghost started going around killing people, just like he did before he was dead. The first people he murdered were the scientists who had cut up his brain. He killed them one after another. Only he didn't stop when he got even with them. He's still out there, walking around in the dark, killing whoever he finds alone in the night. He always moans first, though, because he's in such terrible pain."

After Gator finished his story, nobody said anything. We just watched the fire. Eric was poking at it with a stick. Nobody else moved. A minute passed, then two. I gazed across the field into the darkness. There was a shooting star. Suddenly, from just behind us, a ghost blared an extremely loud and frightening "Mooooo."

We were on our feet quicker than we'd been the night the mountain lion came after us. Without stopping to talk, we disappeared over the top of the hill. And in the morning, when Eric's parents found us sleeping on their front porch, we had to explain to them how. . .

"We woke up early. . . ." "We were just out for a hike. . . ." "We wanted some eggs cooked in the microwave. . . ." I guess we didn't want to scare Eric's parents with any stories about a ghost in their pasture.

The Oakville Hag

*The other kids told scary stories about Mrs.
Orlander. She looked like a witch and they called her
"The Old Hag." Alan Miller even said she ate little
children.*

The Old Hag always laughed when she talked. She
laughed even though there was never anything funny to
laugh at. Even if you just looked at her, she'd start laughing like you were the greatest comedian in the world or
something. And she didn't laugh like other people, either.
She cackled like an old witch.

I could never stand to look at her when she cackled like
that. She'd open up her mouth like she was going to
swallow a bullfrog or something. Then, the most repulsive
old set of gums you ever saw would stick out at you.

It was disgusting. She didn't have a tooth in her head.
Just this grizzled old pair of brown-and-white smackers.
Even when I got to know her a little, I still couldn't stand
to look at her when she laughed. She had the ugliest gums
in the world.

The Old Hag wasn't really a hag, of course. That's just
what we called her because she was so old and ugly and
weird. Her name was Mrs. Orlander. But every kid in
Oakville called her The Old Hag. Even some of the
grownups called her that.

The house where she lived is down by the railroad
tracks at the edge of town. It's really old. No paint. And
out in the back, there's an old barn with its roof caved in.

Everybody says the place is haunted. Lots of the guys say they've seen her walking around in there. Alan Miller said that two nights ago when he walked by the house he heard people screaming.

Whenever I go out to my friend Raymond Olson's house I have to walk right by The Old Hag's place. Back before she died, I used to see her in the swing on her front porch sometimes. But mostly, when I saw her, she would be walking around town.

The Old Hag used to walk all over. I don't think she ever really went anywhere. She just liked to walk. It was part of being weird. She'd walk around in these real old-fashioned clothes that looked like they came from Afghanistan or someplace. And she had this crooked, wooden cane. The way she looked, it's no wonder people called her The Old Hag.

I remember walking along the railroad tracks on the way home from Raymond's place one night. I was all alone and there was just a sliver of a moon poking from behind the clouds. I had just started across the railroad bridge over the creek when I saw somebody standing in the shadows.

Then she laughed and I knew it was The Old Hag. I don't have any idea what she was doing there all alone at night like that. I just remember thinking how small she was. Even if you allowed for her being all bent over and everything, she still wasn't much taller than I was.

Somehow, I wasn't just scared anymore. I felt sorry for her, too, and that was worse than being scared. I opened my mouth to say something. But no words came out. I hurried past her as fast as I could walk without actually breaking into a run. "Hi, sonny," The Old Hag said as I went by. Then she cackled a terrible laugh that sent shivers down my back.

The rest of the way home I kept remembering stories the other guys had told me. Everybody said The Old Hag was a witch. I'd heard all kinds of crazy things. Some of them were pretty gross.

Alan Miller said she ate little children. He said he saw

41

her take a little kid into her house once. Nobody believed him, of course. Alan Miller has an overactive imagination. But the thing is, you start to think. I mean nobody knew what kinds of things The Old Hag really did.

Another time, Alan told me about a big black cat outside his bedroom window. He said it was on the roof yowling at the moon. He said he screamed at the cat to scare it away. But the cat just looked at him in an evil way, like it wasn't afraid of anything human. Alan said the cat's eyes glowed red in the night just like hot coals in a fireplace.

I guess the cat made Alan really scared so he chucked an old boot at it and knocked it off the roof. Alan said he hit the cat right in the face, right between its fiery red eyes. The last he saw of it, the cat was running across his frontyard like the devil was after it.

The next day, Alan saw The Old Hag in town. She had a big lump on her forehead and she was walking with a limp. Alan said she was like that because she was the one who had been outside his window. He said The Old Hag was a witch and she turned herself into that cat whenever she wanted to take on a different form. There were all kinds of stories like that about The Old Hag.

* * *

It was on Halloween—just a couple of months after I'd seen her on the railroad bridge—that we tipped over The Old Hag's outhouse. We also scattered garbage all over her yard, but that was an accident.

Nobody had planned to go over there. We just came up with the idea because it was Halloween and . . . well, there aren't too many outhouses around anymore. Besides, she was the only witch in town.

All of us guys are too old for trick-or-treating. We haven't done any of that for a couple of years. We just go out for the tricks. We never do anything really bad. We just have fun. Everybody does it.

After we tipped over The Old Hag's toilet, Alan Miller

knocked over her garbage can. We were running away. I guess he didn't see it in the dark and he ran into it. Anyway, about a million bottles flew out of the can and scattered all over the yard. A lot of other garbage, too. Alan ended up on the ground right in the middle of it.

The next morning was Saturday. No school. I never gave a thought to The Old Hag's tipped-over garbage can and toilet. After all, we'd pulled a whole lot more Halloween pranks the night before that were better.

After I ate breakfast, I decided to ride out to see my friend Raymond. He lives on a farm a couple of miles from town. On the way past The Old Hag's place, I saw her neighbour, Mr. Moody, out in her yard.

That's when I remembered the outhouse. Mr. Moody was standing right beside it. I peddled my bike faster, pretending not to see him. But it was too late. He had already noticed me. He waved for me to stop.

"Young Stewart." That's what he called me. "Some little ruffians have made a mess of Mrs. Orlander's privy," he said gruffly. "I want you to give me a hand setting her back up."

I parked my bike, smiled, and tried to act cheerful. Mostly, I tried to act innocent. The Old Hag came out. She really did look like a witch. She had a wrinkled face and a long nose and ears so big they looked like they'd come off somebody else's head. When she saw me she started cackling just like always.

Once he had me in the yard, Mr. Moody set me to work like I was his hired boy. We set the toilet back up and fixed one of the door hinges that had come unnailed when the top of the privy hit the ground. Then we fixed the roof where some shingles had come off.

After that, we picked up all the wine bottles and garbage that had spilled when Alan fell over the garbage can. Then we fixed an old picket fence even though none of us guys had knocked it over.

Finally, Mr. Moody couldn't find anything else for me to do so I almost got away. I would have, too, except Mrs. Orlander came back outside just then and started cackling.

She thanked us and told Mr. Moody to come in for coffee.

"You come, too, sonny," she said to me. "I've got some leftover cookies I made for the trick-or-treaters." Then she laughed that crazy laugh again. "Of course, nobody came. They think I'm a witch."

Mrs. Orlander led the way into her house. It was pretty scudzy inside. Dark and grundgy. Everything looked really, really old. We sat in the living room at a table with a white tablecloth over it.

The tablecloth was so clean it looked out of place next to all the grundge. I kept pretty quiet. It was a strange feeling to be sitting inside The Old Hag's house. But the cookies were good. At least they would have been if I hadn't been so nervous. I was worried Mr. Moody would ask me if I knew who tipped over The Old Hag's toilet, so it was a relief when he only drank one cup of coffee and got up to go.

I got up, too, but before I could get away, Mr. Moody stopped me. "Young Stewart," he said, "would you be interested in a job?"

I thought he meant working for him so I said sure. But it turned out he wanted me to shovel snow for Mrs. Orlander. He told me later that if I'd keep her walk clean, he'd pay me a dollar for every inch of snow that fell during the winter.

I don't know why he hired me to shovel someone else's sidewalk, but he did. The first snow came in December. Just a couple of inches. It didn't take long to shovel. Mrs. Orlander came out and cackled at me, but she didn't bother me that much.

About a week later, we had a blizzard. It snowed all day. Eight more inches. Eight more dollars. It only took a little over an hour to shovel it and Mrs. Orlander invited me in for cookies after I finished. I figured Mr. Moody had made a mistake giving me a dollar an inch. Eight bucks for an hour's work and free cookies to boot was pretty good pay for a kid.

Of course, the very next day it snowed another inch. I had to go back over and shovel the whole thing for a dollar. It didn't take as long as after the blizzard. But I still figure Mr. Moody got a little more value for his money than the day before.

Mrs. Orlander invited me in for more cookies after I finished. By that time, I'd almost gotten used to the way she looked. Her laugh was enough to scare a dead rat, but whenever she'd start cackling and showing her gums I'd just look the other way.

There's no getting around the fact that she was pretty strange. I hardly understood anything she talked about. Sometimes it was like she was just talking to herself and I wondered if she even knew who I was. She never called me by my name and a couple of times she called me Jimmy.

The next time I saw her, she gave me a Christmas present. She didn't invite me in for cookies like she'd done before. But just as I finished, she came out on the steps and gave me a new billfold. Genuine leather. It wasn't wrapped up or anything. She just handed it to me. "It's for Christmas," she said. Then she laughed the same old cackle and went back inside before I could thank her.

After that, Mrs. Orlander almost always invited me in for cookies when I went over to shovel snow. Once, she showed me a bunch of pictures. She had them in an old shoebox. A couple of the pictures were of her when she was a little girl. I was surprised how much she looked like a regular kid.

One picture was of a dog she had when she was growing up. It was a collie and it was harnessed to a little homemade sled that you could ride in. There was a house in the background and I recognized it. It was the house she still lived in. "That's this house," I said. "You've lived in this house all your life."

She shook her head. "No, I lived somewhere else for a few years." Then she laughed again. Only this time she didn't laugh as loudly as usual.

She took a picture out of the box and showed it to me. Three people—a man, a woman, and a boy who must have been about my age—were standing in front of another house. Mrs. Orlander said she was the woman in the picture. She didn't tell me who the others were. But you could tell the picture made her sad. She stared at it for a long time.

In the picture, Mrs. Orlander looked happy. She didn't look weird at all. I wanted to ask her who the man and the boy were, but it was just like the night on the railroad bridge. My voice wouldn't work. Mrs. Orlander put the picture back in the box. "There was a fire," she said. Then she put the pictures away.

At the end of March, we had one more big snowstorm. After I finished shovelling, I hung around for a little while, touching up the path to the outhouse. I hadn't seen Mrs. Orlander and I was hoping she'd invite me in for cookies. I figured it was the last snow of the winter so I wanted to say good-bye.

Finally, she came to the back door, but she didn't invite me in. She said she had the flu. She said she'd have cookies for me the next time I came. When she closed the door, she didn't even laugh that crazy laugh.

Of course, there wouldn't be a next time. The snow had started to melt even before I had it shovelled. The next day I went to see Mr. Moody. He was out cleaning his garage when I got there. "Well, young Stewart," he said when he saw me, "have you been keeping track of the snow?"

When I told him we'd had forty-three and a half inches, he said I'd measured wrong. Then he gave me forty-five dollars instead of forty-three fifty. He said that he'd been keeping track himself and we'd had forty-five inches of snow. "You must be trying to cheat me," he said.

Before I left, I asked him about Mrs. Orlander's husband and if they had ever had a kid. I asked if there had been a fire. "As I understand it, there was a fire," Mr. Moody said. "But I couldn't tell you anything about what happened. People said the boy started it. But that was way before my time so I wouldn't really know."

Mr. Moody stopped and looked down at his shoes. With one of them, he scraped a line in the dust on the garage floor. "Mrs. Orlander has had her problems," he said, "but she was always good to me when I was a boy. So were her folks, but that was a long time ago. Mrs. Orlander must be well over ninety years old now. I'm over sixty myself."

I didn't think much about Mrs. Orlander for a couple of weeks after that. It was spring. I had forty-five dollars. Then one day I was uptown and I saw a picture frame in one of the stores. It was the kind with little windows where you put in a whole bunch of small pictures.

I don't know why, but it made me think of all the pictures Mrs. Orlander kept in the shoebox. I decided to buy it and give it to her for a present. First, though, I wanted to take it home to paint my name on the back of it.

I found a brush and a small can of red paint in the basement. As neatly as I could, I wrote "To Mrs. Orlander." I printed my own name at the bottom. Just then my mom called me to supper and I knocked over the paint. It went all over my dad's workbench.

I grabbed a few rags and wiped everything up as much as I could. It took a lot of turpentine to make the red spots come out of the top of the workbench. Then I threw the rags in a corner on top of some old boards.

At supper, Dad asked me if I had remembered to turn off the light. He's always yelling about turning off the light in the basement because the heater runs when it's on. Dad says that wastes electricity.

For once, I had remembered to turn it off. After supper, I went back to see how my picture frame looked. The paint was still wet, but I figured I could take it to Mrs. Orlander the next day after school. On the way up the stairs, I forgot to turn off the light.

That night, it took me a long time to get to sleep. Even after I went to sleep, I kept waking up. I had all sorts of crazy dreams. The last one was about Mrs. Orlander.

She was standing over my bed. Only she wasn't laughing. "Get up, Jimmy," she screamed at me. "Get out of bed. There's a fire." Her voice was like I'd never heard it before. "Get up," she screamed again. "Get up." Then I realized I was awake and she was gone.

There was no point in trying to go back to sleep after that so I went to the kitchen for something to eat. On the way past the basement door, I remembered the light. And as soon as I opened the door, I smelled the smoke. The pile of rags I'd thrown in the corner was on fire.

Dad said I should have called him first. But I didn't. I ran down the stairs and smothered the fire with a pair of old coveralls. Then I gathered up the rags and carried them outside. The smell was terrible. It was so bad my parents woke up.

The next day, I didn't go to school or anything. I just stayed home. About the middle of the afternoon I remembered Mrs. Orlander's picture frame. When I took it over to her house, though, she wasn't home. I even went around and knocked on the backdoor. But nobody was there. Finally, I put the picture frame inside the screen door and left.

On the way past Mr. Moody's house, I saw him standing in the window. He waved at me to stop. Then he came outside. "I'm sorry, young Stewart," he said, "but Mrs. Orlander won't be home anymore. We took her to the hospital yesterday with what we thought was a bad case of flu. She passed away last night."

The funny thing about Mr. Moody telling me about Mrs. Orlander is that I wasn't surprised. Somehow, I already knew it. I never went back to get the picture frame either. I figured it belonged to her.

About a month later, they had an auction sale. They sold everything in Mrs. Orlander's house. I stayed all day and watched them so I know the auctioneer never sold that shoebox full of pictures. And he never sold my picture frame either. I guess that's one reason why, when people say the house is haunted, I think it might be true.

Contact

"It all started with that stupid ghost story for Mr. Mitchell." And it led a young computer buff with a homemade communications program to a chilling, contemporary encounter beyond the world of technology.

This whole thing happened because Mr. Mitchell, our language arts teacher, said we had to write a ghost story. I hate language arts, and I hate ghost stories. My favourite subject is science so I didn't even believe in ghosts. And I sure didn't know any ghost stories. I didn't until tonight anyway.

Computers are more what I'm interested in. My mom got me an IBM clone for Christmas, a Hewitt Rand with a full-colour Packard Bell video display monitor. Six hundred and forty K of memory with a hard disk drive, two floppies, and a modem. It's worth a couple of thousand dollars so it's supposed to be for the whole family. But I'm the only one who ever uses it.

It's in the basement. I'm typing on it now. I come down here every night after school. Because of the modem, I can link up with a buddy of mine named Larry who has a computer and modem too. It's pretty neat how it all works.

Mostly, Larry and I just play games. We've got some first-rate stuff from some of the bulletin boards. I just learned about bulletin boards a couple of months ago. You can get free programs from them or leave messages or ask questions that somebody else using the board might be able to answer. Larry says you can get just about anything you want if you find the right bulletin board.

We've been working on a couple of communications programs of our own from some of the material we picked up on one of the boards. I mean, we're definitely not hackers or anything like that. The Caramilk secret is still safe. But we've come up with some pretty wild stuff all the same.

It's just that I never expected to use a computer the way I did tonight. Before tonight, the most important thing I'd ever done with this thing was my arithmetic homework. Tonight, though, I linked up with a computer at NASA, the "National Aeronautics and Space Administration." I still can't believe it. And that's not all I'm having trouble believing either.

It all started with that stupid ghost story for Mr. Mitchell. It's due tomorrow and I probably should have written it as soon as I got home from school tonight. But I played computer baseball with Larry instead.

Then, after supper, I did my other homework. After that I was going to call Larry again for another game of computer ball, but I stopped when I realized it was already past midnight. My parents had been in bed for about two hours.

The house was all dark except for the light above the computer here in the basement. It was kind of spooky actually. And there was no way around it, I had to write a ghost story, even if I didn't have any idea what it was going to be about.

Then I remembered a bulletin board Larry had told me about. He said it kept files on all kinds of weird stuff. I wondered if it might be able to give me some ideas about ghosts. Maybe even a whole ghost story.

I entered the letters "S" and "T" to call up a communications program stored on hard disk. Then I typed the name of the bulletin board. The computer dialed the number automatically. After a few seconds, the bulletin board menu came on my screen.

I typed in the identification number Larry had given me and pressed the key indicated on the menu for a list of file names. Then things started to happen. I'd never seen so many files. The board had information about almost everything—almost everything except ghosts.

There was a file called "The Dead," though, so I tagged that entry and pushed my computer's "enter" key. "WHAT DO YOU NEED?" came up on the monitor. I typed in the words "Ghost Story."

"PLEASE WAIT" came on the screen and flashed five or six times before the computer beeped. Then the words "SORRY, INFORMATION UNAVAILABLE" came on the screen. I reached to push the "quit" key. But the computer gave two more beeps. "PLEASE WAIT" flashed back on the screen. Then: "LINE CM269372587 ENTERING POSSIBLE SOLUTION NOW."

"WHAT DO YOU NEED?" reappeared on my monitor. I typed "Ghost Story" again. Then the screen began to scroll past several pages of text. It seemed to go faster and faster as it went. It was much too fast to read the text, too fast to even pick out single words. When it finally stopped the computer beeped and the monitor went blank—except for the cursor flashing on and off at the bottom of the screen.

Then the message "WHAT DO YOU NEED?" reappeared. This time, it came one letter at a time, as if someone at the other end of the telephone line were typing it. Again, I typed in the words "Ghost Story" and pushed the "enter" key.

Once more, the response came one letter at a time. "Do you want a particular ghost story or will any ghost story do?"

I typed "Any will do."

The computer answered with the question "Is this for school?"

I typed "yes." Then the computer did something strange. Something it had never done before.

An image came on the screen. It was just a series of coloured dots and it only lasted for maybe a second, but it looked like somebody's face. Not like a real drawing or anything. But it didn't take a lot of imagination to see that it was a woman's face. She was smiling.

The computer beeped three or four times. The screen went blank and the cursor started across the page, followed by the words "Maybe we can help each other."

I knew for sure now that I was dealing with a person on the other end of the telephone line and not just a computer program with a file of stored information. "What do you mean 'help each other'" I typed. Then I pushed "enter."

There was a pause. Then the cursor began to move again. "I have some information I want you to give to someone else. If I can keep contact with you long enough to transmit the data, I want you to call Houston, area code 713, telephone number 555-5843, extension 317. Your identification number will be CM269372587. You can transmit the information via your modem. In exchange for doing this for me, you'll get a ghost story.

"One more thing. Don't give the data to anyone else. Do you agree to my terms?"

With my language arts class less than ten hours away I would have agreed to almost anything for a ghost story. I typed "Yes. But when do I get my ghost story?"

That's when I got my first big shock. "That depends on how long I can keep contact with you. But once you pass the data to NASA you'll get what you need. Only you'll have to write the story in your own words. It will be easy. All you'll have to do is tell what happened."

NASA. I couldn't believe somebody was asking me to pass information to NASA. Who was this person, a foreign spy or something? Why didn't she give them the information herself? And what did she mean "as long as I can keep contact?" Wasn't she on a computer somewhere just the way I was? I began to type quickly. I asked one question after another, as fast as they came to my mind.

She never answered my questions, though. The computer beeped and she took control of the cursor instead. I say "she" took control of the cursor even though I can only guess who was on the line.

The words, "Wait. I haven't much time" came on the screen. "Contact is difficult because it is maintained with

intercepted microwaves and it's hard to contain the signal. This is the first time since the crash I've been able to get even this close to giving NASA the information it needs. Please get ready to save data."

Several pages of material followed. I can't write anything about what it said because I promised not to give the information to anyone but NASA. Besides, the truth is, I couldn't understand much of it anyway. I learned just enough to know that it had to do with the space shuttle program, and I was pretty sure whoever gave it to me was an astronaut. But other than that it was all just a bunch of numbers and formulas.

At the end, the computer screen began to fade in and out. Then, for just a minute, it came back again. "Transmit data to Houston as soon as possible" was typed across the bottom of the screen.

"But when do I get my ghost story?" I typed. The screen began to fade again. Then it came back briefly. "Who do you think you're talking to?" was the only answer I got. Then the screen blinked and we were cut off.

It wasn't until I called Houston that I realized what my ghost story was all about. The phone number I'd been given linked my computer to one at NASA. At the top of the screen were the words "Challenger—collected data on explosion of January 28, 1986."

I didn't try to snoop around in the computer at NASA or anything. I just transmitted the information I'd been given. One thing I did notice was that the number CM269372587 was the identification number of one of the Challenger's astronauts.

When I saw that, and realized who I had been in contact with, a chill went through my body. I remembered the woman's face on my computer screen and, for the first time, understood what she meant when she told me to write what happened.

Agnes and Albert Applebee

Agnes and Albert Applebee were a comical couple who argued about everything. Then one night in a storm they were forced to stop at a large, old farmhouse that Agnes said looked haunted. "Poof-doodle," said Albert, who thought there was no such thing as a haunted house.

Agnes and Albert Applebee were pioneers. But by the time they came to homestead in Poplar Valley, the land close to town had already been settled. They had to go way out on the prairie to build their home and start their farm. They went farther out on the prairie than anyone else had ever gone.

They went so far out on the prairie that there were no neighbours to keep them company. They went so far out on the prairie that when they wanted to buy groceries and supplies for their farm, they had to get up about four o'clock in the morning. Otherwise, they wouldn't get to town in time to do their shopping before the stores closed for the night.

Once Agnes and Albert got to town, they never had time to visit friends or go for a walk in the park. Instead, Agnes and Albert always had to hurry to buy their supplies. Then they would start down the long and winding trail towards home.

You see, it never mattered how early Agnes and Albert left in the morning. It never mattered how soon they got to town. And it never mattered how quickly they loaded everything into their wagon, said "get-up" to their old horse, and started down that long and winding trail across the prairie. They would still never get home until way after midnight. And sometimes, the sun would already be coming up in the morning before they'd get there.

Because the trip took so long, Agnes and Albert only went to town three or four times a year. They lived too far away to go any more than that. Most of the time, they just stayed home. They spent their days feeding the cows, slopping the hogs, and mucking out the barn. Agnes and Albert always had things to do on the farm.

Since Agnes and Albert didn't have any neighbours, the only conversations they had were with each other. Sometimes, in the evenings, they sat and talked about their farm. Sometimes, they sat and talked about what they would do the next time they went to town. But mostly, Agnes and Albert just argued.

They'd start out talking just like anybody else, but before long they'd begin fussing at each other. Then arguing and bickering. Eventually, Agnes would get so mad she'd say, "Albert, there's no more point in talking to you than there is talking to an old cow in the barn."

Agnes and Albert argued about everything. If Albert said the weather would be rainy the next day, Agnes said it would be clear. If Agnes said a fox had been in the chicken house, Albert said that it had been a weasel. If Albert said that a ewe was ready to have a lamb, Agnes said the ewe would not be ready to lamb until the next week.

Every year in the fall, when the weather started to get cold, Agnes and Albert went to town. They'd always buy enough groceries and supplies for their farm to last all winter. That's because, once the snow came, Agnes and Albert wouldn't go back to town again until the snow melted in the spring.

One year, Agnes and Albert had been particularly busy. They'd had a late harvest, and then Agnes decided to build a new hen house. Afterwards, Albert wanted to put in a new corral. One thing led to another. September came and went. Every day the weather got a little cooler and a little cooler.

Finally, one evening Agnes said, "You know, Albert, the nights are getting awfully chilly. If we don't look out, it's going to snow. Then we'll be stuck out here for the winter and we won't have enough supplies for the farm or enough groceries to last until spring. I think we'd better just drop all the work we're doing and go to town."

When Agnes said that, Albert said she was being as silly as a chicken in sneakers. "It's not going to snow yet," he said. "Haven't you noticed there aren't many acorns this year? And the beaver houses aren't very big either. All the signs say we're going to have a warm fall and a mild winter."

Agnes told Albert that, for all the good it did her, she might just as well talk to an old cow as to him. That night, though, after Albert went to bed, he began to worry about getting snowed in.

The next morning before the sun came up, he woke Agnes. They hitched their old horse to the wagon and started down that long and winding trail across the prairie. They rode all morning and almost all afternoon. About four o'clock, they finally reached town.

And that's when Agnes and Albert discovered that day was a holiday. You see, Agnes and Albert lived so far out in the country they didn't know what days were holidays. They didn't have any neighbours to tell them. They didn't know until they got to town that it was Halloween.

Of course, Albert blamed Agnes, and Agnes blamed Albert. When they finally stopped arguing, they saw that the stores were full of people buying candy for trick-or-treaters and buying Halloween costumes for all the Halloween parties. The stores were so full of people it took Agnes and Albert a lot longer than usual to get the supplies and groceries they needed.

By the time they had everything bought and paid for and were outside loading their goods into their wagon, it was starting to get dark. "Oh, Albert, look at that," said Agnes. "The sun is going to be all the way down soon.

We're going to be out there on that lonely old prairie in the dark. And it's Halloween night. Why, I think we had better stay right here in town. We can always go home in the morning."

"What are you talking about?" said Albert. "We've still got an hour of daylight left, and there'll be a full moon tonight. Besides, have you forgotten about all the work we've got waiting for us at home? And on top of that, we've got cows and sheep and pigs and chickens that need to be fed. We need to get home as soon as we can. Even if it takes us all night to get there. We've got to get home and feed those animals."

Agnes knew that Albert was right about the animals so, for once, she only argued for a little while. Then she started helping Albert load their supplies into their wagon. After it was loaded, Albert and Agnes covered the wagon with a large canvas tarp. They tied everything down tightly. When they climbed onto the wagon seat, Albert said "get-up there" to their old horse and they started down the long and winding trail that led across the prairie to their farm.

Agnes and Albert had no more than reached the edge of town when the sun went all the way down. The night was pitch black. It was one of those nights when clouds cover the whole sky so you can't see the moon or the stars. Not only that, the wind came up from the north and started blowing colder and colder.

Then it started to snow, the hard crusty snow that blows in the wind and stings your face when it hits you. Agnes pulled her face lower into her coat. Her nose was cold. Her fingers were cold. Her toes were cold. "Albert," she said, "we shouldn't be out in this weather. Turn around and go back to town."

Of course, Albert was cold, too. But when Agnes told him to turn around and go back he said that that idea was the silliest thing he'd ever heard. "Why should we turn around and go back to town?" he said. "We'll just stop at the next farmhouse we come to and stay there until the storm's over."

Just then, they came over a rise in the road and way back off the trail Albert saw a big old farmhouse that he'd never seen before. The farmhouse was three stories high and its windows were covered with wooden shutters. Albert saw smoke coming out of the chimney. He figured someone must be home. "There's a place to stop right there," he said.

Albert drove the wagon up the driveway to the front door of the big, old house. "Agnes," he said. "You go find out who lives here. I'll take the horse around back and put him in the barn."

"I don't know," said Agnes. "That house looks pretty spooky to me."

"Oh poof-doodle," said Albert. "Just find out who lives here and ask if we can stay until the storm's over."

Albert drove off in the wagon and Agnes walked up to the big wooden front door of the old farmhouse. She saw that it hadn't been painted in several years. Through the shutters, she could see that the inside of the windows were covered with spider webs. A large knocker hung on the middle of the door. Agnes gave it a hard rap.

Suddenly, the door flew open. Agnes just had time to duck as a large owl flew past her into the night. She heard a scream, and then realized it was her own voice. Agnes didn't bother to close the door. She forgot about the snow. She forgot about the wind. She ran to the barn so fast she almost got there before she left the house.

"Albert," she screamed. "That house is haunted. There are cobwebs in the windows. The door flew open all by itself and a bird almost knocked me down. It tried to pull out my hair."

Albert closed the barn door, locking the horse inside. "What are you talking about, Agnes?" he said. "You know as well as I do that there's no such thing as a haunted house."

"Maybe I do and maybe I don't," said Agnes. "One thing I do know is that I'm not going back in that house, so you might just as well get that animal of yours out of the barn and take me back to town."

"And two things that I know," said Albert. "There's no such thing as a haunted house, and we're not going anywhere else tonight."

"Albert," said Agnes, "I might just as well talk to an old cow as to you. If you think you know so much about haunted houses, then you go in that one over there and find out who lives in it."

"Well," said Albert, "I just will."

The front door of the house was still open when Albert got there. He looked in at a large hallway. There was no furniture in the room. The paint on the walls was grey with age. A crystal chandelier in the middle of the ceiling swayed gently back and forth as if it were being pushed to and fro by a breeze.

Albert would never admit it to Agnes, of course, but something about the house did seem strange. "Hello," he called rather quietly. "Is anybody home?"

Nobody answered. Albert turned back to the outside. "Come on in," he said to Agnes. "There's nobody here."

"How do you know that?" said Agnes. "You didn't make but a little-bitty call. If you want to know if somebody is at home in a big house like this one you've got to sing out so somebody can hear you."

Albert looked down the hall to an archway that led into another room. "Hello," he said again, but his voice was no louder this time than before. "Is anybody home?"

"Oh, for mercy's sake," said Agnes coming inside. "Let me show you how to holler."

Agnes stopped and looked at the inside of the house for the first time. She tried to see past the open archway at the end of the hall. "Yoo-hoo," she called in her loudest hog-calling voice. As she spoke, the door behind her slammed closed and the latch fell shut. Agnes and Albert both jumped.

"See what I told you," said Agnes. "This house is as haunted as a graveyard in the woods."

"Shhh!" said Albert. "I think I hear something." Agnes and Albert both listened. They tried to see into the room on the other side of the archway. "Maybe it was just your echo," said Albert. They both took a step closer trying to see into the other room.

Agnes called "Is anybody there?" in a voice quieter than the first time. Still, nobody answered. Agnes and Albert took a step closer. Then another step. Then another. All of the time, Agnes kept saying, "Hello. Is anybody home? Is anybody here?" But nobody ever answered.

After a few more steps, Agnes and Albert were close enough to see into the other room. It was a nicely decorated sitting room. Fine paintings hung on the walls. Chairs and tables were placed conveniently, here and there. Bouquets of flowers were on all the tables. A smouldering fire burned in the fireplace. A grand piano sat in the middle of the room.

But dust was everywhere. It covered the tables. It covered the piano. It covered the pictures on the walls. It even covered the fresh flowers and their vases. Agnes and Albert didn't see anyone so they walked in.

"Hello," said Albert. "Is anyone here?" Nobody answered, but a sliding door in the archway behind them slammed closed.

Agnes jumped, and Albert fainted. Agnes ran back and tried to open the door. It was locked. When she turned around, she saw the image of a man at the other end of the room. He wore tall black riding boots and fine silk clothes. "Good evening, madam," he said. "Welcome to my home."

Even though Agnes knew nothing at all about haunted houses, she knew she was looking into the eyes of a ghost. "Albert," she whispered. "Albert, wake up." But Albert didn't move.

"Never mind him," said the ghost. "He'll get up when he's ready. It has been a long time since I've had visitors. Would you like to hear a song?"

Before Agnes could say yes or no, the ghost walked to the piano and sat down. For the next half-hour he played the most beautiful music Agnes had ever heard. But suddenly, the song changed. Instead of beauty and happiness, the music turned to fear and evil, even murder. Then, in a triumphant thunder, it stopped.

The ghost turned towards Agnes. "You see," he said, "I was born on the prairie. My father worked for the Hudson's Bay Company. When I was five, I was sent to school in Europe. I learned to play music and became a famous concert pianist. I was very rich. But then, the audiences grew tired of me and I decided to return to the place of my birth. I wanted to bring music to the frontier.

"This land was once my father's. I came here and built the house you're in now. I ordered the finest furnishings from Europe. I gave parties and invited the best people from all over the valley to come.

"Then, ten years ago this very night, thieves broke into my house. I wouldn't tell them where I hid my gold so they murdered me. They cut me up into small pieces and threw me into the fire. I never received a proper burial so every year at this time, my bones burn again."

"But why are you telling me this?" said Agnes. "Why don't you tell Albert? He's the one who wanted to come here."

"It doesn't matter who I tell," said the ghost. "The important thing is that I find someone to help me. I want you to dig up the ashes under this fire. They're all that is left of my body. I want you to bury me on the hill behind the house."

"Oh," said Agnes, "I'd like to help you, but I don't know anything about burying people."

When Agnes said that the ghost slowly got up from the piano and started walking towards her. His hands shook as he raised them higher, towards her face. He looked as if he meant to strangle the first person he touched. Terror was in his eyes.

"But now that I think about it," said Agnes quickly, "I'll just bet I can figure out how to bury them ashes if you'll give me half a chance. Just tell me where I can find a shovel and an ash bucket and I'll get right to it."

The ghost brought what Agnes needed. "I'll be on the hill behind the house," he told her just before he disappeared.

When Albert woke up, Agnes was in a frenzy digging the ashes out of the fireplace. "Horsefeathers and bird-radish," he said. "What are you doing now, Agnes? This is no time to be cleaning a fireplace."

"Just never you mind what I'm doing," said Agnes. "I haven't got time for any of your arguments. And if you know what's good for you, you'll get off your bottom and tote this ash bucket out into the yard for me."

Albert took the bucket and followed Agnes through the house and out the back door. They walked across the yard and up a hill behind it. When they got to the top of the hill, Agnes stopped. She couldn't see the ghost, but she knew he was there. She began digging a hole, first in the snow, then in the ground.

When the ashes were buried, Albert and Agnes went back inside the house. The ghost sat at the piano. "Whoooo's that?" Albert asked. Agnes told him to be quiet and listen. The ghost began to play. The music was even more beautiful than when he had performed for Agnes before.

When the ghost finished playing, he thanked Agnes and Albert for burying his ashes. Then, as a reward, he gave them the deed to his house. He also gave them the land that had belonged to his father. And just before he disappeared, the ghost gave them all the gold and silver he had hidden in the secret compartment behind the up-stairs closet.

Agnes and Albert almost never argued after that. They lived together happily from then on. Partly, they were happy because they had all that money. And partly, they were happy because they had that big house to live in, and all that land for their farm. But mostly, Agnes and Albert were happy because they lived so much closer to town than they'd ever lived before.

Buffalo Bones

"Grandpa always said the ghosts of a thousand Indians lived on our ranch. After today, ghosts will be all that are left here."

My grandpa used to tell me about the Indians. He told me how it was in the old days when his father, my great-grandfather, first came to the foothills. Sometimes, he would take me out and show me places on our ranch where Indian people used to camp. He showed me spots where they had built fires and places where he had still been able to find buffalo bones when he was a boy.

Grandpa showed me tipi rings, too. They're big circles of stones the Indians used for holding down the outside edges of their tipis. Grandpa said some of those rings have been here for hundreds of years. Once, he took me up on Culver's Butte to a spot he claimed had been a Blackfoot burial ground.

Grandpa always said the ghosts of a thousand Indians lived on our ranch. After today, ghosts will be all that are left here. We're leaving. The government built a dam and they're going to flood the whole valley. Dad says he's just glad Grandpa isn't around to see it happen.

Actually, we've moved almost everything out of here already. Or sold it. We had a big auction sale last Saturday and got rid of all the cattle and machinery, and most of our horses, too. They even sold the buildings, all except the old barn they say can't be moved.

The first time I heard the sound of the horses was after

the sale. Everyone had gone home and we were sitting at the kitchen table. Nobody was saying anything. Mom was hemming one of my dresses and Dad was drinking a cup of coffee. I think they were sort of in shock because of the auction. I was brushing my hair, getting ready to braid it.

All of a sudden, I heard horses trotting down the lane past the barn. The corral gates were all open so I figured they were heading for the river. I jumped up to look, but when I got to the window there was nothing out there.

The strangest thing about it was that Mom and Dad didn't have any idea what I was so excited about. Neither one of them had heard a thing. I thought they were kidding me at first. After a while, though, I just figured I must have been daydreaming or something. I couldn't think of any other explanation for it.

Then, the very next morning, before I even got out of bed, I heard the horses again. This time I knew they were horses. They had to be horses. I mean, I've lived on a ranch all my life. I ought to know what horses sound like. They woke me up out of a sound sleep, but by the time I got to the window, they were gone again.

That morning, after breakfast, Dad made me clean up all the litter and junk that was left over after the auction sale. I told Dad he was crazy to worry about picking up a little bit of trash when everything was going to end up under forty feet of water anyway. But he didn't pay any attention. Dad has his own way of doing things and if he thinks something needs doing, he has to have it done right then. That's just the way he is.

After I finished cleaning the yard, I took a walk by the river. I figured the horses had gone that way, but I couldn't find any tracks. I looked for an hour before I gave up and went to sit on the rock Grandpa said the river had carried down out of the mountains. It's a huge boulder, as big as our pickup truck. We go down there to fish sometimes. And sometimes I just sit out there and watch the river.

That's what I was doing that morning after I quit looking for the horses. The water was low, the way it

65

always is in late summer. I thought about how, before long, water from the river would cover the whole valley. Our house and barn would be gone. The old lilac tree in the backyard would disappear under a lake. The river wouldn't even be a river anymore.

I closed my eyes and lay back on the rock. I felt the sun in my face. The rock was hot against my back. I think I went to sleep for a minute or two. When I opened my eyes I saw an Indian boy on a horse crossing the river fifty yards upstream. The boy was close to my age or maybe a little older. I didn't recognize him though. He was riding bareback on a small appaloosa mare.

What surprised me most about him was that he was wearing a buckskin shirt and leggings. The way he was dressed, it was just like watching someone from a hundred years ago. I wondered where the boy had come from and what he was doing on our ranch.

I don't think he even saw me. If he did, he never let on. His horse walked carefully in the shallow water until he got to the other side. Then he turned to the northwest, following the river, travelling away from me. About a hundred yards upstream, he turned away from the river.

The boy rode slowly, watching the ground in front of the horse as if he were following a trail of some kind. Then, while I watched, the horse and its rider disappeared over the top of the bluff on the opposite shore.

Normally, I tell Dad right away when I see somebody on our ranch. I didn't do it this time, though. It didn't seem to matter now that the cattle were gone. Besides, Dad had already accused me of hearing things. I didn't want him to say I was seeing things, too.

That night, I had a dream. I dreamed I saw the Indian boy again, riding his appaloosa. Only this time, instead of crossing a river, the boy rode across a huge lake. The water wasn't very deep, barely higher than the horse's fetlocks, but it covered the earth as far as you could see. The boy seemed to ride and ride, but everywhere he rode, there was only water.

That was two days ago. We've been busy since then

packing boxes, getting the last of our stuff ready to move. Mom and I tore down most of the corrals and stacked the posts by ourselves. Dad's been away a lot working on the new house, getting it finished so we can move in today.

Last night I had another dream. This seems crazy, but I'm not even sure it was a dream. Dad didn't get back with the truck until after supper so we had to load furniture and boxes and about everything you can think of until way past midnight. We left our mattresses in the bedrooms so we'd have something to sleep on.

I was pretty tired by the time I got to bed. But I think it was more than just the work that did me in. It was everything. Moving away from a place where I've always lived. Thinking about going to a new school. Living in a city for the first time in my life. I guess what bothers me the most is imagining how it will be to come back to this place when there's nothing here but water.

Last night, after I crawled into my sleeping bag, I thought about all of the times Dad and Grandpa and I had gone up into the hills west of the ranch. Sometimes, we'd go way up into the mountains and hunt sheep. Or maybe we'd go up to the river's headwaters and fish for trout.

Then I started thinking about the horses. It's still a mystery to me what could have made those sounds. I guess that's the last thing I remember thinking about before I fell asleep. The sound of horses. Then I sat up in bed. I could hear them again.

Only this time they were louder. I knew they were more than a bunch of runaway saddle ponies or a few riders out for some fun. This time the sound of the hooves made a roar like nothing I'd ever heard before. I could feel the noise as much as I could hear it. I crawled out of my sleeping bag and went to the window.

Outside, buffalo stampeded through the yard, past where the corrals had been. I could see them all the way to the river and beyond, over the bluff where the Indian boy had disappeared. The moon was bright and the sky was clear. Shoulder to shoulder they ran, one behind the other for as far as I could see. They made the whole world shake under their feet.

I don't know how long I stood there before the herd started thinning out. Clouds of dust floated in the air. But still the animals came. Then I saw the hunters. They were dressed like the boy I'd seen at the river. They were driving the buffalo on. Then, they were gone. I looked out the window, down the lane to the river where our cattle used to water, and watched the dust slowly settle back over the land.

Finally, I crawled back into my sleeping bag. In the morning, I woke up before anyone else and went out into the yard. There were no tracks. I walked towards the river anyway, without really thinking about what I was doing or where I was going.

I waded across to the other shore and followed where I thought the buffalo had gone. I walked up the bluff and cut down the other side in just about the same place I'd seen the Indian boy two days before.

I must have walked for more than an hour. When I came to the end of our land, I just kept walking. At Eagle Canyon, I turned and followed an old trail towards the mountain wall. I hadn't been in the canyon since Grandpa died. He used to take me there to show me eagles' nests.

The canyon was a small one, rocky and not much good for anything except mules and mountain goats. When I got to the canyon wall, I climbed it as high as I could. Then I found a spot on the rocks to sit down. If the buffalo I'd seen in my dream had come here, they would have been trapped. They would never have escaped from the hunters.

I turned and looked behind me in the direction I'd come from. Not far away I could see the river, winding north-west, deeper into the mountains. I realized then that the canyon, too, would soon be flooded.

Below me, I could see what looked like white rocks on the canyon floor. Everything around me was parched brown or red except for the rocks. I worked my way back down and discovered they weren't rocks at all. They were bones. I wondered why we'd never seen them before.

They were half-buried in dead grass and gravel. But they were so white they shone in the morning sun.

I could tell the bones had been there a long time because some of them crumbled when I tried to pull them out of the ground. I managed to dig a couple of them out. But it wasn't until I got home that I found out what the bones really were.

Dad and Mom were mad that I had been gone so long. The truck was all loaded and they were ready to go. Dad yelled at me to hurry. Then he saw the bones I'd brought back. He stopped and took one of them from me.

"Sarah, do you know what you have here?" he said. "These bones must be at least a hundred years old." He shook his head and looked off towards the river. "You've found the last buffalo bones anybody will ever find in this valley."

The Ghost on Rattlesnake Hill

On their way home from the watermelon-seed-spitting contest, driving the old road from New Castle during a thunder storm, Ike and Dave's pickup truck started making unusual noises. It grumbled and groaned and sputtered all the way up Rattlesnake Hill. Then it stopped completely.

Ike Leatherby and his brother Dave had to drive sixty-five miles to Staunton in order to enter the watermelon-seed-spitting contest. Entering the contest had been Ike's idea. First prize was five hundred dollars. Even if they didn't win, Ike figured they'd at least be able to eat a few watermelons. And Ike loved eating watermelons.

As it turned out, neither Ike nor Dave won any money, although Dave's last spit was only seven inches short of taking third place. Both Ike and Dave received a free watermelon just for entering the contest. The melons were the small round ones, but Ike knew that it was often the little melons that tasted best.

On their way home that night, driving the old road from New Castle during a thunderstorm, Ike and Dave's pickup truck started making unusual noises. It grumbled and groaned and sputtered all the way up Rattlesnake Hill. Then it stopped completely.

The pickup was twelve years old and had been due for a tune-up for a year and a half. But Ike hadn't gotten around to it yet. Ike rarely got around to anything until after Dave jawed at him about it for a while first.

"Now what are we going to do?" Dave said when the truck stopped at the side of the road. They were more than ten miles from the closest town. It was the middle of the night, in the middle of the most violent thunderstorm of the season.

Wind made the big oaks and maples along the road bow towards the valley below. Leaves and smaller branches flew through the air in the same direction. Rain steadily pelted the truck. Every few seconds a new bolt of lightning lit the entire sky so that, for an instant, the night would turn as bright as day.

The thunderclaps rumbled so menacingly Ike and Dave sometimes covered their ears. "There won't be any cars on this road tonight," Dave said. "One of us is going to have to get out and walk. We have to find a house where we can use the telephone."

"Who are we going to call at this time of night?" Ike asked. "We're five hours from morning with no place to go. Besides, not many people live out this way. There might not be a house along here for miles." Ike wiggled sideways in his seat, trying to make himself comfortable by maneuvering his fat belly from behind the steering wheel. "When the sun comes up," he said, "we'll see if we can fix this old beast."

After a few minutes, the rain let up and the wind slowed. Lightning came less and less often. "Do you remember a story about a rich lady who was murdered out here somewhere?" Dave asked. "Whoever killed this woman tried to cut her up in little pieces to hide the body. But the police caught him before he finished. I think they found all of her parts, except for her head."

"Don't tell me stuff like that," said Ike. "I won't be able to sleep."

"You won't be able to sleep anyway," said Dave. "Not out here in this storm."

"I can sleep okay when it's raining," said Ike. "And I can sleep okay in this truck. But I can't sleep with you yapping at me all the time."

Ike pulled the two head-sized watermelons he and

Dave had received for entering the contest out of his way and folded himself up on just a little more than his half of the seat. He rested his head against the side of the truck door, trying to make his hat work as a pillow. He wondered if he really could sleep. He tried to think of something other than the storm and the gruesome murder Dave had told him about.

A few minutes later, the last tremendous bolt of lightning lit the sky. Ike saw a large brick building only a hundred yards up the road. "There's a house," he heard Dave say. The rain suddenly slowed to become a drizzle. Dave told Ike they should walk to the house and ask the owner if they could use the telephone.

Ike said that would be foolish. "We can wait here until morning," he said. "There's no point in waking up strangers. I'm not going to do it. I'm not going anywhere until morning. Absolutely nothing is going to make me leave this truck before the sun comes up."

At that moment, an eerie blue light appeared, as if from nowhere, on the seat beside them. Then, before either Ike or Dave could say a word, their pickup truck started to shake from side to side. The doors sprang open and Ike and Dave were thrown onto the road.

Ike, who was normally a slow runner, made it to the house first. But his brother was only two steps behind as they raced up the steps to the front porch.

"What in the blue blazes was that?" Dave said. "Am I dreaming, or did something just throw us out of our own truck?"

"I don't know what happened," said Ike. "And I'm not going back to find out. You can be sure of that. I'm staying right here at this house until morning. There's nothing that's going to get me back to that truck before the sun comes up. And when I say I'm not going somewhere, I mean it."

"We'd better find out who lives here," said Dave as he stepped to the door and rang the bell.

No sooner had Dave touched the doorbell than a light came on in the house. In a moment, the door opened, but there was no one there.

"I don't like this," said Ike. "We'd better go back to the truck." But Dave was already inside. "Oh no you don't," Ike said following Dave into the house. "You're not leaving me out here alone."

Inside, Ike found a comfortable living room with large stuffed chairs and an orange sofa on a white shag carpet. A desk and chair were close to the door. Across the room, a fire burned in a large, stone fireplace. In an adjacent dining room, a large table was covered with a beautiful lace tablecloth and all kinds of good food to eat.

A steaming-hot, freshly roasted turkey sat in the middle of the table. There was a big plate of corn-on-the-cob, a bowl of sweet potatoes, and several different kinds of pies and cakes. Just about everything worth eating was right there.

"Goodness me," said Dave. "Do you suppose somebody has put out all this food for us?"

"No, I don't," said Ike. "You just leave that food alone. It belongs to somebody else and . . . Say, they have watermelon here."

Ike looked around. He didn't see anyone watching. "I guess it wouldn't hurt to have a small piece of watermelon," he said, reaching for the biggest slice.

Dave looked at all the food. Then he sat down at the table. "Pass the turkey," he said.

Once Ike and Dave started eating, they didn't stop until they were full. Dave ate a little of almost everything. But Ike only ate from the large platter of watermelon. He ate all of the watermelon, except for one piece, which he left because he didn't want to make a pig of himself.

Ike was just wondering what they should do next when a strange blue light floated into the room. He could hear a soft hum as the light moved towards him. "It's the same light that was in the truck," said Dave.

"Let me out of here before the house starts shaking," said Ike. But when he tried to run, both of his feet stuck to the floor. He didn't know if they stuck there because of fear or because they were really stuck.

Slowly, the light came closer. When it reached the side of the table, it stopped. Then, slowly, the light changed from an eerie blue illumination to a woman dressed in a long, beautiful, blue gown. The only thing was, the woman didn't have a head.

She sat down in a chair at the far end of the table. Then she spoke—which, if you stop to think about it, is an amazing feat for someone who doesn't have a head.

"Well," said the woman, "I see there's only three of us here tonight."

"That might be true," said Dave, "but if you can wait half a second I'll see to it there's only two of you."

"And I can leave you alone just as fast," said Ike.

The ghost slapped her hands down on the table. "You stay right where you are," she said. Ike could see steam coming from where her head used to be.

"But whooooo are you?" Ike asked.

"Who am I?" said the ghost. "I'm the woman who owns this house. And I'm the woman who owns that food you just ate. Now, I need you two to help me."

"Well," Ike said in a trembling voice, "I don't really think Dave and I can be much help to you. To tell you the honest truth, we're not even much help to ourselves. The best thing is just to look in the yellow pages for some good help. Dave and I wouldn't be any use to you. Why we . . ."

"Keep quiet," said the ghost. "I only get one chance at this every seven years. I was buried without my head and I can't rest until I get it back. It's buried somewhere in the basement of this house and I want you to go down there and find it for me."

"Oh no," said Ike. "I'm sure we wouldn't be able to find any head down there. Why, Dave says that I can barely find my way out of bed in the morning."

"If you don't find my head," said the ghost, "I'm going to take yours."

"Whoa now," said Ike. "We'll take a look. Maybe we can find that head. You never know until you try. That's what I always say. You never know until you try. Where's your basement? We'll just go down there and take a look."

74

The ghost led Ike and Dave to a door near the fireplace. "The basement is through there," she said.

Ike opened the door. Then he screamed and jumped back, slamming the door closed again. "Why, it's pitch black down there," he said. "It's darker down there than a whole stack of black cats. I can't go down there looking for somebody's head. Why, a person could lose their mind in that much dark and never find it again."

"You're likely to lose more than just your mind up here," said the ghost.

Ike thought about it and decided the ghost had a point. Slowly, he began to open the basement door again.

"Don't be such an idiot," said the ghost. "There's a light switch at the top of the stairs. Just turn it on before you go down."

Ike and Dave went down into the basement. They began digging and searching for the ghost's lost head. They dug and they searched and they searched and they dug until Ike found what they were looking for just before the sun came up in the morning.

When Ike and Dave took the head upstairs, the ghost was waiting in a chair beside the fireplace. "If you're sure you want to give it to me," she said, "just put the head here on my shoulders."

"Oh, I'm sure I want to give it to you all right," said Ike stepping forward with the head. "I don't have any use for spare heads."

Ike reached to put the head on the ghost's shoulders. But as he looked closely at it for the first time, he realized he had his own head in his hands. "No," Ike screamed. "This one's mine," and he pulled it back from the ghost.

The ghost jumped from her chair, grabbed the head, and tried to pull it away. "It's too late," she said. "You've already given that head to me."

"No," said Ike. "It's mine."

The ghost let go of the head and grabbed Ike by his shoulders. She began to shake him the way she had shaken the truck. She shook him and shook him. "Wake up," she said in a deep voice. "What are you talking about? Wake up. The sun's up."

Ike opened his eyes. Dave let go of his shoulders. "Boy," he said, "you must really want that watermelon. I wasn't trying to take it away from you. I was only trying to wake you up. It's morning, and there's a big brick house just up the road. We can probably use a telephone there."

The Ghost of Plum Valley

You won't find Plum Valley on any map. No one lives there anymore. But people say if you go there at midnight on Halloween, a ghost from the past will come back to haunt you.

Up on the border between Manitoba and Saskatchewan there's a ghost town called Plum Valley. Not much of the old townsite is left anymore, but if you go there you'll be able to find where Plum Valley used to be.

You'll find a dead end street along an abandoned railroad right of way. There'll be a few hedges and shrubs that have gone wild. If you get out of your car and walk in the grass at the side of the road, you'll discover the rocky foundations of buildings long ago burned or torn down. Dust and tumbleweed will blow in the wind where a whole town of people once lived.

There was a time when Plum Valley was a thriving community. At its peak, about 1920, the town had four general stores and three grain elevators. It also had a lumberyard, a post office, a couple of restaurants, a blacksmith shop, a hotel, a school, and two churches. Various other shops and stores had been opened. And a merchants' association had been formed to attract more businesses to the town.

On Saturdays, farmers for miles around Plum Valley came to shop there. Whole families gathered with their neighbours on street corners to gossip and discuss the week's news. For a few years, Plum Valley even had its own newspaper.

Bert Snyder ran the paper. Before coming to Plum Valley, Snyder had worked as a reporter on several big-city dailies in the East. Gradually, he drifted west. In Plum Valley, he started his own paper. As a sideline, he ran a printing business.

Snyder's dream was to see Plum Valley grow into a major trading centre. He hoped that one day he would be able to open a livestock auction. He thought it would bring more people and money to the town.

According to a rumour, Snyder had originally come from New York State. Some people said he had been a railroad brakeman there. According to one story, he had once made a careless mistake that caused a train to crash. Several of the train's passengers had been killed.

That, according to some, was the reason Snyder often seemed so nervous and preoccupied. That's why he carefully watched every train that came through town. He could never forget the accident he had caused.

Snyder lived with his wife and daughter in a big house at the end of Main Street. It was directly across the street from the railroad tracks. Beyond the house lay the open prairie. Since Snyder often had trouble getting to sleep at night, his habit was to take long walks along the tracks before going to bed. Unless the moon was bright, he always carried an old-fashioned kerosene lantern.

One Halloween night, Snyder became particularly restless and uneasy. He was alone in the big house at the end of Main Street. His wife and daughter had been away visiting relatives, but they were due back on the midnight train. Late that evening Snyder left his house, as usual, for a short stroll in the night air before going to the station to wait for his wife and daughter.

There was no moon that night. As Snyder walked, a stiff breeze blew clouds across the sky and a chill into his body. A half a mile outside of town he passed a string of half a dozen empty railroad cars that had been left on the siding to be loaded with grain at the town's elevators. Near where the railroad siding joined the main line, Snyder stopped at the spot where he planned to build his auction ring.

He turned his light to shine across the empty lot, imagining once again just how he would build the corrals and livestock barn. Then Snyder turned back to the railroad tracks and looked south, away from the town. He buttoned the top button on his jacket and resumed his walk.

After only a few steps, however, Snyder stopped. In the dark, he examined the switch between the main line and the siding. It had been left open. Snyder recognized the mistake immediately. The brakeman on the evening freight must have forgotten to close it after the empty boxcars had been diverted onto the first siding.

Snyder knew the midnight passenger train was due to arrive in Plum Valley. His wife and young daughter would be on that train. Because of the open switch, it would be diverted onto the siding. In the dark, it would crash into the boxcars waiting silently on the tracks.

Just then, in the distance, Snyder heard a mournful whistle. He turned. There, little more than a mile away, he could see the single light of the passenger train coming towards him in the night.

Snyder grabbed the switch handle and pulled with all his strength. But it was no use. The switch was locked in place. There was no time to go for help. He grabbed his lantern and stumbled towards the oncoming passenger train, waving his light madly in the air.

As the train passed Walker Road, its whistle blew again. Snyder was at the coal yard now. He stopped by the water tower and waved his lantern back and forth in the night to warn the train's engineer of the danger waiting ahead. But the train kept coming.

Snyder swung himself up and climbed to the tower's watering platform. He leaned out over the tracks, holding on with only one hand, while he waved his lantern. Frantically, he tried to get the train to stop. Back and forth. Back and forth. Snyder swung his lantern wildly in the air.

The train was almost upon him when he lost his grip and fell from the tower. At the same instant, the train's engineer realized the light ahead was on the tracks. He pulled the emergency brake and the train skidded to a stop less than a hundred feet from the boxcars blocking the siding.

Bert Snyder had saved the train. But it had cost him his life. People said the fall alone probably killed him. His mangled body, missing several parts, was found along the tracks near the train. By the time of his burial, most of Snyder's remains, except for his head, had been found.

In the years after the accident, Plum Valley's population began to dwindle. Snyder's widow and daughter were the first to move away. After a time, others followed. Another town nearby built a livestock auction. Not as many farmers as before came to Plum Valley to shop on Saturday afternoons.

Businesses began to close and move to other, more prosperous towns. Finally, the grain elevators in the town closed. Then the school and the post office shut their doors for good. The last of Plum Valley's citizens moved away and the buildings that were left were eventually torn down or burned.

If you should go back to Plum Valley today, all you will find is a dead end road and a few chunks of cement and rock buried in the grass nearby. People say, though, if you come at midnight on Halloween night and stand on the old railroad right of way, you can look south beyond Plum Valley's old Main Street, and you'll see a light.

Some people say that light is a ghost train that haunts the old railroad line. They say that when you see the light you should run away as fast as you can. Because if you wait long enough to hear the long, sorrowful whistle of the ghost train, the engine will stop and, helpless to resist the lure of that other world, you will board the train and ride it through the night, forever.

But most people say that the light is something different. They say if you see it, you should stay where you are. Slowly, the light will come closer and closer. Then, if you listen carefully, you will be able to hear a low, painful moaning in the dark ahead of you. Some people say you might even hear someone crying in the night.

Before the light reaches you, it will stop, then slowly fade away, until finally you won't be able to see it anymore. People say that that light is Bert Snyder. They say he returns every year on Halloween to look for his head.

The Ghost of Peppermint Flats

No one can disprove the existence of ghosts. Even the fiercest skeptic sometimes fears the night. "The one thing I am sure of," says the adult narrator of this story, "even after all these years—and even knowing what really happened that night—I never go around Peppermint Flats after dark."

I have no idea what people see out at Peppermint Flats. They think it's a ghost. They've been talking about ghosts for seventy years. They've been talking about ghosts for so long nobody remembers how they first started talking about them.

I'm not saying there isn't anything out there. But if you want to hear the true story about Peppermint Flats, I'll tell it to you. All that talk started when I was just a little girl going to the old one-room schoolhouse that used to be there. It was in the fall of 1919, at Halloween.

Our teacher, Mr. Otis, was just a young man. I didn't realize that at the time. As far as we children knew, he was just an odd, funny-looking teacher. We didn't care if he was twenty-five or fifty. We just did our lessons and, when he wasn't looking, made fun of him.

Mr. Otis was tall and lanky, with a long neck and an Adam's apple that bobbed up and down when he talked. He looked just the way I thought Ichabod Crane, the teacher in *The Legend of Sleepy Hollow*, would look. I could imagine Mr. Otis, too, being chased by a headless horseman.

It's one of the things in my life I'm ashamed of now, but I used to laugh at Mr. Otis just like the other children. He was such a nervous man it was easy to make fun of him. Sometimes when we were all reading our lessons, and Mr. Otis was studying his law book, the room would get especially quiet.

That's when somebody would be sure to knock a book off their desk. Mr. Otis always jumped when it banged against the floor. Or one of the boys would let a cat loose in the school. Mr. Otis hated cats. I think he was afraid of them.

Of course, I never played any of those kinds of tricks on Mr. Otis. But I laughed when the other children did. And in the end, it was I who did him the most harm. I never meant to. He just made me mad. He had hurt my feelings and I wanted to get back at him. I wanted to make him look foolish.

Our school had been getting ready for a Halloween party. We had dances and suppers and various kinds of social activities all through the year at Peppermint Flats School. At Halloween, there was always a party because we were country kids. We lived on farms, too far apart to go trick-or-treating the way most children do today.

I was eleven that year. And Mr. Otis embarrassed me in front of the whole class because I believed in ghosts. Maybe I didn't really believe in ghosts. But people were generally more superstitious back then so the possibility of ghosts didn't seem unreasonable to me. Mr. Otis disliked superstition, though. He had given us a lecture just that morning about more modern ways of thinking.

We children were putting up decorations, getting ready for the Halloween party that night. I didn't even know Mr. Otis was listening. But he overheard me tell my friend Maggie Jamison how I was afraid to walk past the house where Emily Cooper had burned up in a fire. Nobody lived in the house anymore and I told Maggie it was haunted.

I think I understand now, but at the time I didn't know why Mr. Otis got so upset with me. He grabbed my arm and marched me back to my desk. "That's just childish nonsense," he said. "There aren't any ghosts in that house."

Everybody in the school stopped and watched as Mr. Otis sat me down in my chair. He gave me a little shake as he did it. I can still feel the way my head bobbed back and forth.

I was tall for my age and quite grown up. At least, that's what I thought. To have Mr. Otis treating me like a small child in front of everyone nearly brought me to tears. I'd never been in trouble for anything in school before, but he made me stay at my seat for the rest of the afternoon.

I hated Mr. Otis for that. I sat in my chair, thinking how I'd been mistreated, while everyone else put up decorations for the party. I never thought about Mr. Otis being good friends with the Coopers. I never thought about why he might be upset. I only knew that he had treated me harshly for a minor transgression, hardly a transgression at all.

That evening, while I was at home getting ready for the party, I came up with a way to get even. I had planned to go dressed as a duchess. My costume included a long, nearly transparent, cotton scarf. As I sat in front of my mirror, I pulled the scarf so that it covered my face like a veil. I smiled through the cloth at my ghostlike appearance.

I knew right then what I would do. That night, while Mr. Otis introduced the students who were to give the recitation of Washington Irving's *The Legend of Sleepy Hollow*, I'd appear outside his window. I'd gaze at him through my veil. I'd be an apparition in the night.

It would be dark, of course, but I knew that if I held a candle close to my face under the veil I would be illuminated in a particularly ghostly way. He wouldn't be able to see my face well enough to recognize me. He would think he was seeing a ghost.

Everybody was there that night. All the parents and the children from across the district. When it came time for the nine-year-olds to recite *The Legend of Sleepy Hollow*, I slipped out the schoolhouse door. I walked along the side of the building until I came to the window next to where Mr. Otis was standing.

In the shadows, I pulled a candle and matches from my pocket. I lit the candle and held it under my veil just below my face. Then, I stepped to the window. I had only stood there a few seconds when Mr. Otis glanced towards me. I gazed back at him intently. He stopped, and then stared.

At that moment, the flame from my candle must have brushed my veil. Suddenly, the cotton scarf became a blaze of fire. I saw a look of horror come to Mr. Otis's face as he stumbled backwards. At the same instant, I tore the scarf from my body and hurled the flames into the night.

The flames had singed my face and hair, but I was all right. I could hear people shouting in the school. I was afraid and ran to the outhouse to hide. I could hear grown-ups and children in the schoolyard. "I saw it," Mr. Baxter, the school board chairman said. "It was a light. It came to the window." Someone else said that whatever it was, it was on fire.

I slipped from the outhouse. Everyone was looking at a light a mile or more off, across the mint farms. It was in the marsh, but it seemed to be fading away. "That's it out there," people said. "That's the light."

Inside, Mr. Otis sat by the stove. He had fallen and cut the back of his head. My friend Maggie told me he had cried "Emily" at the window before he stumbled off the stage. No one else had seen a face, but lots of people had seen the light from the fire. George Woodruff even said he had seen a second fire in another window. And Mabel McWilliams said she had seen a banshee.

There was a lot of talk after that about ghosts. I was too afraid to tell anyone—even my friend Maggie—what I had done. And I thought Mr. Otis was different after-wards. When he came back to school he had a faraway look in his eyes, and for some reason, the sound of dropping books didn't bother him at all. It was almost as if he didn't hear them.

Right after Christmas vacation, a new teacher came to

Peppermint Flats. My mother said that Mr. Otis had gone away to law school. No matter where he went, I never saw him again. And as far as I know, nobody else around Peppermint Flats ever heard from him after that either.

People's imaginations would never let something like what happened that night at the school come to an end. In the years that followed, they continued to talk about the light Mr. Otis had seen. Occasionally, usually near Halloween, other people would see a light, too.

Lately, it seems to me that somebody is seeing a strange light out there every few months. My own theory is that automobile headlights are somehow reflected in the night, probably from the interstate highway three miles away.

Perhaps, it only happens when the atmosphere is a certain way: on cloudy nights or when the temperature is just right. But for whatever reason, people are still claiming to see that light. They've had the newspaper and television come to report on it a couple of times. Charles Kuralt from CBS News even went out there.

For all of these years—ever since Mr. Otis went away— there have been times when I get a feeling way down inside. I get a feeling that Mr. Otis died after he left Peppermint Flats. I know better, of course, but I get a feeling that the light people see out there is him. I get a feeling that he has come back to look for Emily's ghost.

Or maybe he's looking for me. I don't know. The one thing I am sure of, even after all these years—and even knowing what really happened that night—I never go around Peppermint Flats after dark. All that talk has made me nervous.

Luke Curtis Finds a Cure

In both folklore and fiction, characters who find themselves in graveyards late at night often mistake human beings for spirits. "Luke Curtis Finds a Cure" is a hilarious retelling of this common folk theme.

Ninety years ago, Hickory Hollow was an even quieter place to live than it is today. The people there were blessed with good soil and a favourable climate. No one had to work hard to make a living.

Even among the easygoing folks of Hickory Hollow, though, Luke Curtis seemed exceptional. Everybody said that he was, beyond any doubt, the laziest man in the entire county. "Hard work might not kill you," Luke used to say, "but I've never heard of anybody resting themselves to death."

Luke and Mabel had a little place out on the edge of town, up near the cemetery. The farm didn't amount to much, but they always grew enough food to get along. Luke worked in the garden when he had to, and every year he put in a small tobacco crop to sell at the local auction.

Luke and Mabel had only two children, boys named Will and Tom. As the boys grew older, Luke put them to work. For a time, the farm began to prosper. People began to say that old Luke had developed a smattering of ambition. Before long, however, Luke decided that he preferred

89

getting Tom and Will to do the work rather than bothering with any of it himself.

One morning after breakfast, he asked the boys to hoe the raspberry patch. Instead of going along to help, he took a small sack of persimmons out to the front porch. It was a warm, sunny day. He could hear mockingbirds in the tulip trees. The old hound dog, Josh, was asleep on the road. Luke sat down in a chair and decided to give up physical labour for good.

From that morning on, old Luke never did a lick of work around the place himself. Instead, he told Tom and Will what to do. Once, he tried to tell Mabel, but she didn't care for the suggestion and hit him over the head with the cream pitcher.

Luke spent most of his time out on the front porch eating pecans and persimmons. Depending on the time of day, he'd occasionally move to another spot on the porch where there was more sun, or more shade. But that was as strenuous as anything Luke did.

"What's wrong with you, Luke?" Mabel would say. "Why, you never do anything around here except sit on the porch in the sun like a dried-up old turnip."

"It's the lumbago," Luke would answer. "And the rheumatism, too. They both got me and they won't let go."

Luke claimed the lumbago pain in his back had flared up so badly he didn't dare aggravate it with so much as a minute's worth of exertion. He said the rheumatism in his legs and joints became more painful every day. He said that it hurt him to even stand up. And after a while, he gave that up, too.

Whenever he needed a change in scenery, Luke had Will and Tom carry him around in his chair. Sometimes, he would get the boys to load him into the wagon and take him to town for a soda pop at Clancey's Store. He enjoyed seeing the sights and hearing the local gossip. But most days, Luke stayed home on his front porch sucking on persimmons and watching old Josh scratch fleas.

Mabel was uncharacteristically sympathetic to Luke's infirmities. "There's nothing wrong with that lazy, no-good, rotten pole-cat that a bonfire under his chair wouldn't cure," she told Tom and Will. She said the pain in Luke's back gave her a pain in the neck. "In fact," she said, "the pain is somewhat lower than my neck."

For two years, Mabel tried to get Luke to go to the doctor. "If them diseases bother you so much," she said, "you should get some medicines from Doc Crawley to cure them."

"They wouldn't do no good," said Luke. "There ain't no cure for rheumatism and lumbago except rest."

"If rest were a cure," said Mabel, "you'd be the healthiest man in six counties."

As much as possible, Will and Tom tried to stay out of their father's way. "Hey there, boys," he'd say when he saw them, "carry my chair down to the other end of the porch for me. The sun's too bright here." Or, "Look here boys, did you clean out the barn yet? We've got a new mule coming tomorrow and I want you to plow down the tobacco field."

One day, instead of waiting for their mother to convince old Luke to go to the doctor, Tom and Will decided to see Doc Crawley themselves. "There's got to be something we can do to get the old man going again," said Tom. "Otherwise, we're liable to end up lugging him around forever."

The old doctor considered their problem. "No standard medication is going to cure your father," he said. "What Luke needs is a jolt of some kind to get him started again. Something to make him want to get up and do something. Your mother's idea about the fire under his chair is a good one, except you'd probably burn the house down."

The doctor reached into his black bag and took out a medicine bottle. "This might do the trick," he said. "In small doses, it's only a mild laxative, but if you can get him to drink the whole thing it should be enough to make him want to take a trip or two to the privy. Just make sure nobody's around to carry him and my guess is he'll go on a hike by himself."

That afternoon, while Mabel was away in town, Will and Tom had a fight to see which one of them would take their father a tall glass of iced tea, mixed with the suggested medication. Both were afraid to do it alone so they finally compromised and went together. "Why, look at that," said Luke when he saw the tea. "I do believe that's just what I need to make me feel better."

"I hope so," both brothers said at once. Then they went into the house, and a few seconds later snuck over to the barn so they wouldn't be around when their father needed assistance. They hid in the loft and watched out a crack in the door that offered a clear view of the family privy.

Luke, however, had had a somewhat harder day than usual sitting on his front porch. He yawned and then placed his glass of iced tea on the floor under his chair. Then, he took a short nap. A little while later, Mabel returned, trudging through the heat carrying a fifty-pound bag of sugar home from the store.

Dust rose from the sun-baked dirt in the yard as she approached the front porch. Stepping over old Josh, she struggled up the steps where she spied the iced tea sitting under Luke's chair. Mabel put down the bag of sugar, picked up the glass without waking her husband, and gulped its contents. Smiling to herself, she put the empty glass back and went inside.

It was nearly half an hour later when Will and Tom, still up in the hay loft, heard the back screen door bang shut. Through the crack in the loft door, they saw their mother trotting briskly down the path to the privy. Several minutes later they saw her return to the house, and then jog back to the privy a few seconds after that.

Several more times the boys watched their mother go up and down the same path. Finally, Tom and Will came down and sat on the back steps to wait for her to return, once more, from the outhouse. When she got back, they saw that she was as pale as a ghost. Sweat clung to her forehead and cheeks. "Gee, Mom," said Will. "What's happened to you?"

"I don't know," Mabel said. "It must have been something I ate in town." Just then, from the other side of the house, they heard their father calling. "Boys," said the familiar voice. "Could you bring me another glass of that iced tea?"

Later that same day, Will came up with another idea for getting their father on his feet and off their backs. "You know that old dog, Topper, of Alice Faye's," he said. "That dog looks more like a wolf than a wolf. What we should do is tell Dad there's been a timber wolf around killing calves and sheep. And then tell him it attacks people, too.

"After that, we'll sneak Topper over here and let him go near the corner of the house behind the porch. When Dad sees him he'll be so scared he'll make a run for the front door. But we'll have it locked from the inside so he'll run clear around the house looking for a way in. Or he'll climb a tree or something trying to get away. Whatever he does, it's sure to get him on his feet for at least a little while."

"That's not a bad idea," said Tom. "But you've forgotten one thing. Alice Faye won't care anything at all about us taking her dog. Why, if something happened to that dog while we had him here, we'd be as good as dead ourselves."

"Nothing's going to happen to that old dog. We'll only take him for a couple of hours."

But Will had forgotten one other thing. Luke's .38 calibre pistol. When Topper came around the corner of the house, Luke took one look and didn't ask questions. He shot a hole in the side of the house, blasted a flowerpot off the porch railing, blew over a lawn ornament, and fired three more rounds into the dirt in the yard.

Even if he'd had more shells in the gun Luke would never have hit the dog because Topper had his tail between his legs and was half a mile down the road towards town after the first shot. Luke's old hound, Josh, was ten yards ahead of him and didn't come back for three days.

That night, Will and Tom walked into town to buy a soda at Clancey's Store. "We ain't never going to get Dad off his can," Tom said as they walked along in the dark. As the boys approached the cemetery, they both became quiet. They'd lived down the road from the graveyard all their lives, but it still made them feel uneasy to be there at night.

There was no moon and gusts of wind rustled the leaves in the trees and made the branches moan and groan above their heads. As the boys approached the cemetery gate, they looked up and saw something large and white in the distance. It seemed to be floating towards them from the darkness in the graveyard. Then two more forms, perhaps twenty yards behind the first one, appeared.

What the boys didn't know was that an old white stallion and two young mares had escaped from Harry Clements's barnyard corral earlier in the evening. They also didn't know anything about the hole that had been dug for Moe Preston's funeral. All the boys knew with any certainty was that something large and white was coming towards them out of the dark, with two more apparitions close behind.

And as they watched, the white ghost in the front ran over the hole dug for Moe Preston's funeral and dropped out of sight. The fall broke the horse's front legs and the poor animal cried out in a terrible pain. As the deathly sound faded in the night, Tom and Will raced for home. There, as soon as they could catch their breath, they told Luke and Mabel about the ghosts they had seen in the graveyard.

Of course, old Luke always figured he knew more than anybody else. When he heard Will and Tom's story, he said they wouldn't recognize a real ghost if they saw one fly up the chimney. He said that, in all likelihood, the only thing they'd seen on their walk was an early evening fog. Or maybe an old sheet blowing in the wind.

That was old Luke's first mistake. He didn't stop there, though. He went on to tell Tom and Will that he was sorry he wasn't able to walk. He said that, if only he could walk, he would go over to the cemetery and prove to them that whatever they had seen wasn't a ghost.

When Will and Tom heard that, they offered to carry the old man over to the graveyard right then. They not only offered, they picked up Luke's chair and carried him out the door before he had a chance to come up with an excuse for not going.

In a few minutes, Tom and Will were sneaking along the back of the cemetery fence, carrying old Luke, and heading for the spot where they had seen the first ghost disappear. In the dark, listening to the wind, Luke began to lose some of his certainty about the lack of ghosts in the area. He hadn't been away from home at night in several years and it made him feel uneasy to be carried in his chair through the darkness.

By this time, Harry Clements, along with a neighbour, had tracked his horses to the cemetery. Moments before Will and Tom arrived carrying their father in his chair, the two men had found the old stallion in Moe Preston's grave.

Clements had already examined the horse's two badly broken front legs. He stood over the grave shaking his head, knowing the injury would mean the end for the old stallion. If it hadn't been for the caragana bushes between Clements and the fence, Tom, Will, and old Luke would have been able to see him standing there.

The two boys lifted their father over the fence and set him on the ground beside the caragana inside the grave-yard. In an open area of the cemetery on the hill above them, the two young mares trotted out of the shadows. The wind blew harder through the trees. Will and Tom nudged their father and pointed at the two ghosts.

On the other side of the bushes, Harry Clements saw them too. "Well," he said to his neighbour in a voice the wind rustled and carried clearly to Luke and his two sons. "We'd better shoot the old boy here and then try to round up the two young ones."

Figuring they were the young ones, Tom and Will tumbled over the fence, scrambled to their feet, and were halfway down the road on their way home when Tom remembered their father. "What about Dad?" he yelled to his brother as they ran.

From two steps behind them came a reply. "Never mind about me, boys," said old Luke. "Just pick up your speed a little or get out of the road. My rheumatism's cured."

Ted Stone is a writer and storyteller currently living on Salt Spring Island in British Columbia. His other books include *It's Hardly Worth Talkin' if You're Goin' to Tell the Truth* and *Hailstorms & Hoop Snakes*, which was short-listed for the 1984 Stephen Leacock Award. *The Ghost of Peppermint Flats* is his first collection of stories for children.